Abraham's journey
from Haran to Canaan

Chelsea

24

W · E

S

Abraham and Lot at
the Jordan valley

Jacob's return home —
his meeting with Esau

The hill of Golgotha —
where Jesus died

Bethlehem — where
Jesus was born

Beersheba — the home
of Jacob

MAP OF PALESTINE
(Canaan of Old
Testament Times)

GOD IS ALWAYS WITH US

A Word of Explanation to Parents and Teachers:

This book is part of the New
Curriculum for The United
Church of Canada.

This is a reading book
planned for primary
children of ages 6, 7 and
8, or Grades 1, 2 and 3.

This book is for use in
the home and in the Sunday
church school. It will be
used by child, parent and
teacher.

The primary program is a
three-year program. There is a
teacher's guide for each year. There
is one reading book for each
year.

This book is for the
curriculum year entitled,
GOD AND HIS PURPOSE.

THE   NEW CURRICULUM
THE UNITED CHURCH OF CANADA

GOD IS ALWAYS WITH US

by Audrey McKim

Illustrated by Geoffrey Goss

A reading book
for
the primary child

his parents

and his teacher

● AUDREY McKIM, the author of this book, is a well-known writer of books for children. She is probably best known as the editor of World Friends, a United Church magazine for children ● GEOFFREY GOSS, the illustrator, is a professional artist living in Oakville, Ontario ● JOHN WILKIE, an ordained minister of The United Church of Canada, has acted as biblical consultant ● WILLIS S. WHEATLEY, art director for the Department of Sunday School Publications, has supervised the design and illustration ● GORDON JOHN FREER, editor of the book, is editor of children's publications, Department of Sunday School Publications ● PETER GORDON WHITE is editor-in-chief, Department of Sunday School Publications, The United Church of Canada.

First Published September 1964

(first printing, 115,000)

THE UNITED CHURCH PUBLISHING HOUSE
TORONTO   CANADA

To
Cathy and Elene
Jennifer and Nancy
Kerry, Fraser and Bruce

CONTENTS

chapter 1

THE WORLD AROUND US

This is the planet where you live.

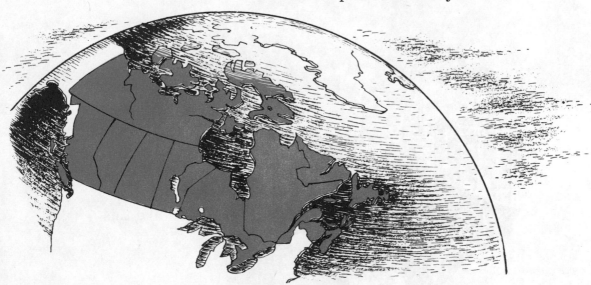

On this planet you live in this country.

In Canada
 you may live on a farm
  like this

or,
 in a town
  like this

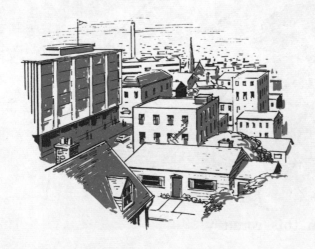

or,
 in a city
  like this

Perhaps you live in a family
like this

or like this

You may go to a church
like this

or this

or this

Perhaps you look like
one of these boys

or one of these girls

Whoever you are,
wherever you are,
you are God's child;
you live in God's world
and God has a purpose for your life.

Do you ask questions
    about your world?
      about God?
        about yourself?
If you do, you should enjoy this book.
It is a book about Jon and Susan.

As you read, you will learn of the questions Jon and Susan ask and of the answers they are given.

You may be asking the same questions, too. In GOD IS ALWAYS WITH US, Jon and Susan discover that the Bible has many answers for many important questions.

In reading this book you, too, may be helped to understand the Bible better and so come to know more about the wonderful life God has given you.

chapter 2

NEW IDEAS FOR JON AND SUSAN

It was very quiet in the room.

Suddenly there was a loud ringing noise near by. Mr. Grant jumped to his feet. His book fell, almost hitting Jon on the head. Jon and Susan jumped too and looked around the living room with startled eyes.

Mr. Grant followed the sound, but Jon was ahead of him.

"It's behind the sofa, Dad! Look! An alarm clock!"

Mr. Grant laughed. "Now isn't that just like your mother? Before she went out this evening she knew I'd forget your bedtime. I suppose she didn't expect that you'd remind me either, so she played a trick on us."

Jon laughed too, but Susan gave a deep sigh.

"I wish bed were as nice at night as it is in the morning," she said. "Maybe it will rain and we can sleep in tomorrow."

Jon didn't want to go to bed either. He cocked his head to listen. "Say, Susan, you might get your wish! The wind is rising. Hear it? What makes it blow, Dad?"

"Wind is moving air," replied Mr. Grant. "A change in the weather causes the air to move. But come on, now. This is hardly the best time for a lesson about the wind. It's bedtime!"

"But Daddy," said Susan, "I thought it was God who made the wind blow."

Father sat down again suddenly looking somewhat puzzled.

Susan was glad to have him sit down. She climbed on the arm of his chair as he began to answer her.

"I mean that in our world we see certain laws working that God has established and that through these laws God is at work. We can't see God, but we can see his work and can see what he is doing. We do not see God creating a sunset but we see that sunset, the result of his work."

"But how do you know that the laws are God's laws?" asked Jon. "How do you know that they are anyone's laws?"

"Well, take the matter of the alarm clock," replied Mr. Grant. "It tells you of two people tonight, but right now you can't see either of them. It tells you that someone put the clock in this room. It also tells you that someone made it. So it is with the world. Because it is here it tells us of Someone who put it here, even though we can't see that Someone."

Jon's eyes twinkled. "That alarm clock doesn't prove that Mother put it here tonight. It could have been someone else."

"Quite right, Jon. It could have been someone else. But it *was* someone. The wind doesn't tell us what God is like, but it does tell us that Someone is behind it. And we believe that Someone is God."

"Like the wind," said Susan as she ran to the window. "I can't really see the wind, but I can see the branches of the trees moving. Something I can't see is at work out there."

"I don't mind too much not being able to really see the wind," said Jon. "But I wish I could see God. Don't we ever see God, Dad?"

"Someday we may see God," answered Mr. Grant. "I think that is part of what we mean when we say we believe in heaven. We believe that there will be a time when we may really see God and know him face to face. But we also believe that while we can't see God now we can nevertheless know him now. We believe that God does let people know what he is like. The big word that describes this is the word *revelation*. God does reveal or show himself. This is what the stories in the Bible are about. In those stories we have people telling us what they have seen or known of God.

"The best story in the whole Bible is the story about Jesus Christ. We believe that in Jesus Christ, God actually came to earth to show us that he is a God who cares for us, that he is a God who loves us. The Bible doesn't tell us all there is to know about God, but it does tell us all that we need to know and are capable of knowing. We believe that to see Jesus Christ is to see God and to see him is enough."

"But I've never even seen Jesus," Jon shook his head.

"You haven't seen him as the people who lived in Palestine

8

saw him. But you can see him in a different way. You can read his story in the Bible. You can learn about the love he showed to people and the faith he taught and lived. And that, I think, is the best part about Jesus. It is not necessary that we know what Jesus actually looked like. That isn't the important thing. The important thing is to know Jesus' love and faith, to know that the love we meet in Jesus is like God's love. The wind tells us that Someone is behind it. Jesus shows us that the Someone is the God of love."

"Oh Daddy, that's an awful lot to understand all at once," said Susan.

"Indeed it is—for one night! So up the stairs we go!"

"I don't think I get it yet, either, Dad," Jon said as he followed Susan and his father into the hall. "But it has sure helped to talk about it. Maybe I'll understand better when we talk together again."

"You can learn something new about God every day, Jon." Mr. Grant took the steps two at a time.

"Then that's what I'm going to try to do."

"Me too!" said Susan who had reached the top step first. Then she remembered the alarm clock. "Oh, I wish right now we could play a joke on Mother! But I'm too sleepy to think of a good one! It really is time for bed!"

You might like to read from your Bible:

> *Genesis 1: 1—2:3 (A story of*
> *faith in God as the Creator)*
> *Psalms 148 (An ancient hymn*
> *of praise to God)*

chapter 3

ONE OF GOD'S BEST IDEAS

"Hurry, everybody!" called Jon from the living room. "Dad and I are ready to light the fire."

"Supper's ready too." Susan came from the kitchen carrying a plateful of hamburgers and sliced tomatoes.

"I've been waiting for this moment all day," said Mrs. Grant as she followed Susan. She put the glasses of milk on the low table in front of the fire-place. "It's been such a dull dark day—just the right kind on which to have our first autumn fire."

"I'm glad we're having supper early so we can watch TV when we're through," said Jon as he waited for his mother and Susan to settle down on the rug. When they were ready he lit the paper lying under the kindling and logs.

The flames mounted and soon the wood fire crackled and began to burn steadily. Mr. Grant gave a prayer of thankfulness to God for the food and for his family. Then Susan passed the hamburgers. There was silence for a few minutes as the family ate and watched the leaping flames.

"I sure wish we could eat in here every night." Jon gave a happy sigh. "Only I'd like to watch TV while we eat, the way the Duncans do."

"Then, I'd never know what had happened to you during the day," said Mr. Grant. "None of us would have a chance to talk."

Mrs. Grant nodded, saying with a smile, "And when would I be able to teach you table manners?"

Jon shook his head. "Learning manners isn't any fun! Neither are rules like having to eat at the table instead of eating and watching TV at the same time."

"I know." Mr. Grant nodded. "When I was your age our family had a rule I hated."

"What was it?" asked Susan as she reached for her glass of milk.

"It was a hard one. One summer I had to come in an hour earlier than the rest of the children, and go to bed. I'll never forget the sound of them having fun outside when I was upstairs in bed."

"Poor Daddy!" said Susan. "I never thought Gran could be so mean!"

"Well Sue, in those days I was a skinny little kid who played so hard all day that I couldn't unwind and get to sleep unless I came in early. My mother, your Gran, enjoyed being out in the garden at that time of evening, but she would come in with me, see that I had a cool bath, and then she would read a long story to me. By that time I was ready for sleep."

"Oh." Susan looked thoughtfully at him as she passed around the hamburgers again. "I guess Gran didn't like coming in any better than you did."

"No, she didn't. And even though I thought she was being unfair to make me come in, I knew she loved me and was doing what she thought was best for me."

"You sure aren't skinny now, Dad," said Jon as he prodded the fire with one of the irons.

Susan laughed. Then she sighed. "Did God make it a rule that mothers and fathers were to make rules for their children?"

"I wouldn't say it that way," said Mr. Grant smiling. "But I do know God's love for me was shown through my mother's love when I was that skinny little boy. It is God's will that children have grown-ups to love and care for them."

"The Duncans don't have many rules in their house," said Jon. "Don't Mr. and Mrs. Duncan love their kids?"

Susan gave a little toss to her head. "The Duncan's house is always in a muddle!"

"Love is shown in many ways," said Mrs. Grant. "Each family is different and sometimes each makes different rules to suit it."

Mr. Grant stretched out his long legs as he finished a second hamburger. "Six children in a family might make a difference in rules."

"Mrs. Duncan puts the two babies to bed around supper time, doesn't she?" asked Mrs. Grant of Susan. "Mr. Duncan helps with the supper. I suppose he finds it less confusing to let the four older children watch television as they eat and while their mother is upstairs with the babies."

"He's a good guy," said Jon. "He took us kids on a hike on Chuck's birthday. We sure had fun with him."

"Yes," said Mr. Grant, "and that was his one day off. You boys didn't know that he gave up a golf tournament so he could celebrate Chuck's ninth birthday with him."

"Mrs. Duncan makes the best Hallowe'en outfits on this street," said Susan. "Donna always wins first prize at the Hallowe'en party." Mrs. Grant looked at Susan. "Yes, a family of six takes a lot of love and care, and maybe a tidy house isn't as important as a mother taking time to play with her half-dozen children."

14

Susan felt sorry that she had mentioned the untidy house.

"Well," said Jon, "I'm glad there are some rules in our house, but I'd still like to eat this way every night and be able to watch TV as much as I liked!"

Mr. and Mrs. Grant laughed.

"If you did it all the time you might turn around and say, 'Mother, how come we never eat in the dining room any more? Why can't we eat there? It would be much more fun!' "

"I'd never say that!" Jon grinned.

Mrs. Grant went into the kitchen and came back with apple dumplings! They were quiet for a while, enjoying the apple dumplings. Then Susan said suddenly, "Mother, Daddy told us the other night that God who made us is a God of love. He must like seeing us tonight eating our supper together around the fire and having such a happy time."

"I'm sure he must," said Mrs. Grant.

The family were quiet; Jon and Susan looked at their mother's and father's faces in the glow of the fire. They watched the flames curling around the logs and they breathed in the scent of the burning wood.

Jon said, "God's idea to have families was one of his best, that's what I think!"

You might like to read from your Bible:

*Ephesians 6: 1-4 (A child's
obedience to his parents)
Deuteronomy 5: 16 (One of the
commandments)*

chapter 4

A PROMISE FOR JIMMY

"But Mother, you'll miss seeing Jimmy Duncan!" Susan could not keep from showing her disappointment. "I thought your cold would be better and you could come to church today. Jimmy will look so cute!"

"Sure, with those little ears that stick out and that wispy hair that stands straight up!" Jon laughed as he thought of the youngest Duncan.

Susan had to laugh too. Jimmy was a favourite with every boy and girl on the street. "And Daddy will miss the service too," she went on. "I wish he didn't have to be away this week-end."

Mrs. Grant nodded even as she tried to repress a sneeze.

"Jimmy is a dear baby, and your father and I are sorry to miss his baptism. You and Jon will have to tell me all about it when you get home."

"We'll tell you everything!" Susan promised as she finished her breakfast. "I hope he doesn't get scared."

"A church full of people won't worry Jimmy," said Jon. "He's used to a house full of Duncans. Oh, look at the time! Hurry, Sue, if you're coming with me."

Susan followed her brother into the hall.

"What does baptism mean, Mother?" she asked as she searched for her rubbers.

"It is a very important service, Susan. A promise is made. You and Jon listen carefully and tell me afterwards what you heard. Don't be so busy watching little Jimmy that you don't hear the words."

"But what if Jimmy cries?"

"That won't matter. Mr. and Mrs. Duncan will be listening to the words spoken by Mr. Fisher, the minister. So will the people. Babies are not expected to be quiet. It is nice if they are, but we don't worry if they happen to cry."

"The Duncan kids are going to sit upstairs in the front row of the gallery," said Jon, putting on his coat. "I wanted to be with Chuck, but today our class sits together in church. Chuck has to help Donna and his aunt keep the four other kids quiet. Oh, hurry up, Sue, or we'll never get there!"

Two hours later Jon and Susan came rushing in to see their mother. Susan could hardly wait to tell what had happened.

"Jimmy was as good as he could be," she said happily. "And his cheeks were pink from sleep and he stared at everybody, and the Duncans were good, too, up in the gallery. I could see them. And Miss Hansen, my teacher, was there too!"

"I tried to listen to Mr. Fisher," Jon said. "Does baptism mean that Jimmy is a member of the church now?"

"Yes, Jimmy is God's child as we all are. God's love is for him too."

"No matter whether he knows it or not?"

"God's love is free and unearned, Jon."

"Oh. As far as I could make out Mr. and Mrs. Duncan promised to teach Jimmy about God so that he would learn to love him, and they promised to bring him to church as he grows up."

"The people stood up and promised too, Mother," said Susan. "Even I did, and my Sunday school class. When the minister asked us if we would help Jimmy to grow up in the church we all stood up together to show that we were willing. But I'm not sure just what it all means."

"If you promised to help Jimmy, you'll have to behave yourself, then," said Jon with a grin. "No more quarrelling with Donna Duncan in front of Jimmy!"

"Oh, Jon!" Susan tossed her hair. "Donna's too bossy! But you were supposed to promise too! Wasn't he, Mother?"

"Yes he was—as a member of the church."

"See!" said Susan triumphantly. Then she added, "Well, I wish I knew exactly what we promised."

"Let me see if I can explain it simply," said Mrs. Grant. "Jimmy's mother and father promised to teach him about God's love. That means they promised to give Christian love to Jimmy, and as he grows to help him grow in his understanding of God.

18

It is good that children know they have parents who love God, and who love their children. It is good that the children are brought into the church where other Christians will also love and help them."

"I see," said Jon. "The people in the church make a promise every time someone is baptized."

"Did they promise for me, too, when I was a baby?" asked Susan looking surprised.

"Indeed they did!" said her mother.

"Do they keep their promises?" asked Jon quickly.

"Many do, Jon. Sometimes there are people who take such promises lightly. They don't think seriously about what God expects them to do. But there are those in the church who so live that the children grow up surrounded by Christian love."

"You know, Mother," said Susan thoughtfully, "the church is like a family, isn't it? Jimmy is part of the church family. So are you and Jon and I . . . Daddy too, Mr. and Mrs. Duncan and all those others in church. And God is the Father of everyone of us!"

Jon nodded. "I think I knew this before, but listening to the service—what's its other name, Mother? The sacrament? Yes, after being a part of the sacrament this morning, it was much easier to understand. And I did promise with the people to—to, well—love Jimmy and help care for him. I promised without thinking too much, I guess. But I'm thinking now!"

———————

You might like to read from your Bible:

> *Mark 10: 13-16 (A story of*
> *Jesus and his love for children)*

chapter 5

WANTED–A LEADER FOR TEN BOYS!

"Telephone, Jon!" called Mrs. Grant from downstairs.

Jon, who was in his room with Chuck and Mark, took the call on the extension.

"Hi Jon! This is Larry!" said the voice on the phone.

"Hi Larry! It's Larry Fisher, fellows," Jon told the others. Chuck and Mark crowded close. They were expecting this call.

"Is it bad news?" asked Jon as he tried to hold the receiver so the others could also hear.

"Yes, my dad just got word that Ticker really does have to leave tomorrow for Switzerland to buy more watches. Then he goes to open a new business in another town."

Loud groans answered this news. Ticker was the name the boys in the Messenger church group called their leader, young Mr. Alex Lemke.

"There goes our hike to the coal mine!" said Chuck. "I knew we'd never get there."

"And our baseball games," said Mark.

"And our play about Nehemiah that we were going to put on for the Sunday church school," added Chuck.

"Quiet!" said Jon. "Say, Larry, hasn't your father got someone to take Ticker's place? He should know *somebody*! After all, he's the minister."

"Dad's trying to get someone. But he had trouble finding a man last month for Tyros and someone for the older fellows. He doesn't sound hopeful. I've got to hang up now. Dad's going to start phoning again."

Jon put down the receiver. He and his friends went back to play with the electric train, but it wasn't much fun any more. They were sorry at the thought of losing a good friend. Then there was the fact that all the plans they had made in their group would fall apart if no one was found to take their leader's place.

"Can't your dad take over, Jon?" asked Mark.

Jon shook his head. "Dad has to be out of town at different times during the week. He couldn't be sure about being regular. What about your dad?"

"My dad says I'm hard enough to live with without taking on nine more. That's supposed to be a joke!" Mark grinned. "But my dad doesn't go to church much."

"Chuck?"

"Dad's teaching in Sunday school and he's got two other church jobs. One's in Family Life. He's much busier than either of your dads."

"How do you know? He is not!" Jon was annoyed.

"Perhaps Mr. Fisher will find somebody before next Friday," said Mark. "Somebody should be able to help with us."

But as the days went by, the boys began to think that their group would have to be divided up and put in with the two other groups of Messengers. They were good groups but were made up of six- and seven-year-old girls and boys. Ticker's group had only eight-year-old boys.

Tuesday, Wednesday, and Thursday went by with Larry Fisher reporting every morning at school. No one had been found. On Friday morning, the day the group met, there was still no news.

"Do we turn up at the church today?" asked Jon of Larry.

"Sure, Dad says we meet. He has an appointment but he will try to wait for us and see that we're all right."

"I'm not going," said Mark. "I don't want to go into any of those other groups."

"Well, I'm going," said Chuck. "I want to see what happens. Then I'll decide whether or not I'll stay."

So after school, the boys appeared at the church. It seemed strange not to be welcomed by Ticker. It was Mr. Fisher, the minister, who was there instead. He met them with a broad smile.

"Any minute now," he said, "you'll be seeing your new leader! Mr. John Rogerson phoned at one o'clock today. He has agreed to take on the job of keeping you fellows in action."

"Who's Mr. Rogerson, Dad?" asked Larry.

"He's a new member from Winnipeg."

"Has he any kids our age?"

"No, but he has one boy who will be in a few years."

"How'd you get him?" asked Larry.

Mr. Fisher laughed. "I didn't. He came to me by phone! You see, he was in our church the Sunday morning your little brother Jimmy was baptized, Chuck. Remember? Well, Mr. Rogerson said that as he took part in the service, and as he promised with the congregation to support Jimmy with Christian love and example, he remembered all the other times he had made that promise at baptismal services. Especially, he remembered the baptism of his young son!"

The boys looked puzzled—all of them but Jon. He remembered what his mother had said about people and promises made in the church.

Mr. Fisher continued.

"Well, to come to the point—Mr. Rogerson decided that he would phone me when he was settled in his work here in town, and offer to help with boys and girls. But Mr. Rogerson hardly had the words spoken when I said, 'Can you come this afternoon at five?' It seemed like a miracle when he said yes! And here he is now! Boys, meet your new leader, Mr. John Rogerson!"

The boys turned and took one long look at the pleasant face of the man in the doorway whose hand was raised in greeting.

Jon, Chuck, and Larry grinned at one another as they went forward to meet him. Mr. Rogerson looked as though he might be all right! And the first thing they were going to do was to find a good nickname for him.

chapter 6

MISS HANSEN

Susan banged the door behind her as she came in from school.

"I don't like Miss Hansen any more," she told her mother. "She kept me in to do a page in my reading workbook all over again. Linda's page was just as messy as mine. Miss Hansen didn't keep her in! Miss Hansen's mean!"

"Oh?" Mrs. Grant stopped beating some egg whites and followed Susan into the sun porch. "You've always said Miss Hansen was very fair."

"Well, she's not!" Susan flung herself down in an easy chair. She wiped angry tears from her eyes.

"Isn't Linda the little girl who is so nervous?"

"Yes, she's jumpy and her printing is awful, Mother. Honest it is. She can't keep on the lines and her letters are all sorts of sizes. I'm a much better printer than she is."

"Miss Hansen must have been disappointed to see a page of careless work when you can print so well."

Susan opened her mouth and then closed it again.

"Is Linda good at any other work?" asked Mrs. Grant as she sat down beside Susan.

"Well yes, she's the best at arithmetic."

"Then I suppose Miss Hansen expects her to do her best work in arithmetic."

Susan thought for a moment.

"Yes, I guess she does. Yesterday Linda had to do her arithmetic over again. Miss Hansen said Linda was careless and shouldn't have made any mistakes."

"Did Linda have more mistakes than you yesterday?"

"No."

"But Miss Hansen didn't make you do your work over again, yesterday."

"No!" Susan almost shouted the word. "I really tried hard. Miss Hansen was pleased with my arithmetic!"

"Of course she would be pleased if you tried hard and did better than you usually do. Miss Hansen expects each of you to do your best work, doesn't she?"

"Yes, but . . ."

"What is easy for Linda isn't easy for you."

Susan's face brightened.

"And what's easy for me isn't easy for Linda! Oh, I guess Miss Hansen was fair yesterday and today. It would have been mean of her to keep me in yesterday when I tried so hard. But today," Susan grinned slowly, "today I wanted to get through fast so I could read my library book. I finished way ahead of Linda. Mother, my page was messy!" She jumped up. "And am I ever hungry!"

Her mother laughed as they went back into the kitchen. Soon Susan was having a snack of ginger snaps and milk.

"I'm glad Miss Hansen is helping you so much," said Mrs. Grant as she went on making her cake. "God has given us all special talents and abilities. It is the teacher's work to help you use them."

"Are talents the things that are easiest and most fun for us to do? Like me with printing and reading and keeping things tidy and playing the piano?"

Her mother smiled. "Yes, and good teachers like Miss Hansen help you make the most of your talents. A good teacher wants you to do your best, but she won't expect you to be best in everything —just to do your best."

"I'd like to be a teacher when I grow up," said Susan. "Perhaps that's what God wants me to be."

"Perhaps so. God will expect you to use your talents in the best way. If you become a teacher, he will want you to help your pupils to do the best they can. His love will come to the children through your love and care for them."

"Oh!" Susan thought about this for a moment. "Miss Hansen is showing God's love for us every day. That's why I like her so much! I do, Mother. I love Miss Hansen!"

chapter 7

GIFTS THAT COST MORE THAN MONEY

"It seems early but have any of you started making plans for Christmas?" asked Mr. Grant as the family sat at dinner one evening.

"Oh, dear," answered Mrs. Grant, "we did agree, didn't we, not to get into a last minute Christmas rush."

"What bothers me is how I'll ever get enough money for all the Christmas presents I've got to buy," said Jon. "I've been saving my allowance, but I've not nearly enough to get gifts for all of you and Gran and Chuck and Mr. Kulak, my teacher. How am I ever going to get decent presents for such a crowd of people?"

His father thought for a moment.

"You'll want to buy some of your gifts, of course, but there are other ways of giving gifts at Christmas—more important ways that don't need money at all."

Jon stared at him.

"How, Dad?"

"Well, let me ask you a question first. Why do we give presents at Christmas?"

"Oh, because other people give us presents. No," Jon shook his head quickly, "that doesn't sound like a very good reason. Let me think! Well, we're celebrating the birth of Jesus. We give gifts on birthdays, so at Christmas we give gifts to Jesus. But that doesn't sound right either. How can we give gifts to Jesus now?"

"I know how," Susan put in. "Miss Ames says Jesus taught that we can show our love for him by showing our love to people. He also said we should love and help each other. I guess giving gifts is one way to do that."

Mr. Grant nodded. "You're both right. We may give gifts to Jesus when we give gifts to each other. So, Jon, in planning gifts try thinking of some of the ways you can make people really happy. What can you give to really show your love?"

"But Dad," protested Jon, "that's what I want to do, but I don't have enough money!"

"Well, let's think about Gran. What special gifts would she like from us? I'm planning on giving her a new electric blanket. She needs one. That will take money, but I want to give her something else, too." He thought for a moment. "I know! I know what she would like from me. Some of my time!"

"Time?" It was Susan's turn to stare.

"Yes!" Her father looked pleased at the idea. "Gran can't read very much because of her eyes. I'm going to hang a Christmas card on the tree. In it, I'll promise to give her at least one hour every week for reading aloud to her."

"Oh Daddy!" exclaimed Susan. "Gran will love that! Maybe I'll give her some of my time, too. Gran likes to hear what I'm doing in school and other places. I'll try to remember interesting things to tell her when she asks, instead of saying, 'Oh, everything's fine.'" Susan stopped. She looked rather thoughtful. "Gran's so good to me, I guess I should do that anyway."

Jon didn't say anything for a while. At last he spoke slowly. "Since Gran hasn't been well, there are lots of things I could do for her on Saturday mornings. I could bike over there and be her handy man for a couple of hours, doing things like shovelling snow and going to the store."

"But Jon, that's when you practise your hockey," Susan reminded him.

"Yes, but I can go to Gran's early. Practice isn't until ten-thirty. Two hours every Saturday would be a good gift of my time for Gran, wouldn't it, Dad?"

"Indeed it would!" said Mr. Grant. "It's a generous gift for a boy to give. You might find it hard to do, Saturday after Saturday."

"I'd be glad to do it for Gran!"

"It would be a gift that certainly would show Gran how much you loved her," said his mother.

"Mother!" Susan's face was bright again. "I've thought of a good idea! You know how much Gran loves to knit. Well, we are to give White Gifts at church for children who need some people to give them presents. Couldn't I buy some wool for Gran with my gift money? It would still be a Christmas gift to her even though I gave it early, wouldn't it? Then Gran could knit mittens and we could give them as a White Gift from the both of us. Gran could show me how to embroider them too."

"That's a wonderful idea!" said Mrs. Grant. "Gran would love to share with you in giving such a gift. Real Christmas giving should be done at any time—not just at Christmas."

"Sue will be giving to two people!" said Jon. "She will be using some of her money to buy the wool for someone she'll never meet, and Gran will have fun with the knitting too."

"Yes," said Mrs. Grant, "the little girl who receives the mittens will know that somewhere there are friends who cared enough to buy some wool and make a gift for her. In this way both Gran and Susan will be helping God show his love for her."

Jon asked to be excused from the table.

"I'm going to make a list of friends and relatives and put a White Gift on the list too," he told his family. "Then I'm going to think of Christmas presents. With the money I've saved and some bright ideas, I'll be able to think of lots of things to give and to do for Christmas gifts."

"Me too!" Susan jumped up knocking over a chair in her hurry. "I've an idea for a gift for you, Mother, and one for you, Daddy! Don't ask me what they are! I won't tell!"

The fun and joy of Christmas planning had begun.

chapter 8

GOD IS ALWAYS WITH US

Susan met her father at the door.

"Daddy, Mother is over at the Duncan's. Chuck got knocked down by a car after school today. Everybody is scared about it. Jon's gone upstairs and won't let me in his room."

"I'm sorry to hear such bad news," said Mr. Grant as he hung up his coat. "Jon will be upset and worried. Chuck is one of his best friends. I'll see if I can help him." And Mr. Grant hurried upstairs.

Jon opened the door slowly. His face was pale and his hands were trembling.

"I'm so sorry to hear about Chuck," Mr. Grant said as he came into the bedroom. "Is he badly hurt?"

"The doctor doesn't know what the injuries are yet. But Chuck's still unconscious. Dad, the guys ganged up on him and were pushing him around. They were real mean! They pushed him out on the street and a car came around the corner and . . ." Jon could not go on with the story.

Mr. Grant put his arm around Jon's shoulders and they sat still for some time.

"Why were the boys angry at Chuck?" Mr. Grant finally asked.

"Well—you know how Chuck sometimes brags that he can do everything better than anybody else—well, Jim and Mark had some kind of puzzle that they were showing the gang, when Chuck came up and said he knew how it worked. He grabbed it away to show everybody, but he couldn't do it after all. Then the gang started to shout at him, calling him Know-It-All-Chuck, and Mr. Big Shot. Chuck pushed Mark. Mark pushed him back, and then Jim did, and all the rest pitched in. It wasn't fair. All those guys against one! They pushed him out on the street and—and

then it happened. Boy, are they all scared now! They don't know what's going to happen to them."

"Where were you, Jon, when all this was going on?"

"Me?" Jon's pale face slowly turned red. "I—I was watching."

"Isn't Chuck your friend? Shouldn't you have been standing by his side?"

"But Dad," protested Jon, "Chuck and I had an argument just before that. He makes me so mad sometimes."

"What was your argument about?"

"Oh, that he had struck more home-runs than I had this past week."

"Had he?"

Jon did not answer for a moment. "Well, I guess he had, but he didn't have to rub it in."

"How did you feel when you saw the boys pushing him around?"

"I didn't like it." Jon stopped suddenly. Then he went on slowly. "Well, I guess maybe I thought it was coming to him. Oh Dad—if I had helped stop those guys maybe Chuck wouldn't have been pushed out into the street. He's big and it takes a lot of them to push him around. If I'd been at his side they wouldn't have picked on him. Am I to blame, too, for what happened?"

Mr. Grant thought for a moment. "I think we *are* to blame when we stand by and let people be pushed around. We don't have to push other people around to do it, but we should let them know what we think is right or wrong."

Jon sighed.

"I can't see how I'm going to wait to find out how Chuck is. What if he gets crippled? How can I stand it, Dad? I like Chuck, honest I do. He's lots of fun even though he is such a big blow. Will it—will it help to ask God to make him better?"

"It will help a great deal to pray, Jon."

"What kind of a prayer should it be? Should I just say, 'Please God, let Chuck get well again soon.' "

Mr. Grant slowly shook his head.

"It isn't quite that simple, Son. Tell God how sorry you are that this happened. If you think you did wrong, ask God to forgive you. Then ask God to keep Chuck in his care."

"But what if Chuck doesn't get better?"

"Jon, when things go wrong because people haven't done the right thing, they must learn to take the consequences."

"Then," protested Jon, "it doesn't really help to pray to God!"

"Yes, indeed it does. God has promised that he will always be with us even when we have done wrong and are in trouble. Knowing this can help us through. Chuck is in trouble because he is full of pride in himself. The boys are in trouble because they quarrelled and lost their tempers. And you feel you are caught up in this trouble because you know you were rather glad to see Chuck being picked on, and because you did nothing."

Jon turned his head away.

"Now is the time for you to have faith in God," his father told him. "It will be hard waiting to hear the news about Chuck. But if you pray, the waiting will be easier and even if the news should be bad, you will be able to stand it, for God will be with you."

"Oh Dad, I don't see how I can stand to wait—now that I think I'm partly to blame!"

Mr. Grant nodded. "Have you heard the story of the first rainbow?"

"The one that came after the big flood in the Bible?" asked Jon.

"Yes. That story was told to answer the question about what happens to people who have brought trouble upon themselves by their misdeeds. The beautiful rainbow that appears after storms is caused by light shining through raindrops, but it was chosen as

a symbol of God's promise that he would be close to us always; and God being with us, we can come through stormy times like this one of yours now, no matter what happens."

There was silence. Then Mrs. Grant's voice was heard below, calling them to dinner.

Mr. Grant rose, smiling.

"Your mother must be home! How about dinner now?"

"You go down first, Dad," said Jon. "I'll be along in a few minutes."

"Of course, Jon. We'll wait dinner for you." Mr. Grant left the room, closing the door quietly behind him.

You might like to read from your Bible:

> *Romans 8: 31-39 (God's love keeps us safe for ever)*

chapter 9

AN ADVENTURE WITH GOD

"I don't want to move away from this street," protested Susan. "I know everybody here. I don't know anyone in Gran's part of town!"

Jon nodded, frowning.

"I don't want to move away from Chuck Duncan. Since his accident we have been better friends than ever. And I don't want to go to a new school either. It's going to be awful!"

"But children," Mrs. Grant looked worried, "Gran is ill. We haven't room in this house for her and she has asked us to move in with her so we can help care for her. We love Gran and believe that it is the best thing for us to do."

"I'm sorry Gran is sick," said Jon, "but that doesn't mean I have to be glad because we've got to move."

"It is a hard move for us all, Dear. I do hope you won't be too unhappy." The phone rang and Mrs. Grant left the room to answer it.

There was a short silence. Jon and Susan did not look any happier. Mr. Grant, who was taking down the curtains, shook his head thoughtfully.

"I'm going to have to do a lot more gardening at Gran's," he told them. "And I'll miss my walk to and from the office. I'll have to battle with traffic every night and morning."

"See!" said Jon to Susan. "Poor Dad doesn't want to move either."

"Now, I didn't say that!" Mr. Grant turned around, his arms full of curtains. "I was just mentioning the things I wouldn't like about the move. There may be all kinds of interesting things waiting for us at the other side of town. But one thing's sure. This move is something we do as a family, and your mother and I hope you will understand why we feel it is right for us to do it."

"I'm not going to like it!" insisted Jon.

"Me neither!" Susan punched a cushion on the couch.

Mr. Grant dropped the curtains over her and sat down to rest. Susan's rumpled head appeared and she sneezed.

"Those curtains will need to be cleaned before they're stored," her father said. Then he added, "Let me tell you the story about a man who believed that God wanted him to move far away to an unknown land. His neighbours thought he was very foolish to do it."

"Is it a story in the Bible?" asked Susan as she settled back to listen.

"Yes, and this is it."

Abraham's Great Adventure

Thousands of years ago, in the city of Haran, there lived a man called Abraham. He and his brothers owned large flocks of sheep and herds of cattle. Often they moved from place to place to find fresh pasture for their animals, but always they had a good home and were wealthy men.

Out in the hills Abraham wondered about God. The people of Haran knew that there must be a power greater than themselves and so they worshipped the moon as a god. They built a great temple in her honour and worshipped there. Abraham worshipped the moon-god too, for he had been told of no greater god. But he thought that surely there must be a more powerful God; a God that had made the moon and the heavens and earth. So he thought and wondered for many years about God.

One day he felt God was very near to him and as he waited quietly, he heard God's voice within his own heart say: "Go from your country and your kindred and your father's house to the land that I will show you."

Abraham made preparations for the journey. His family and friends could not understand why he wanted to leave a safe and comfortable home and go into an unknown land at the command of an unknown God. But Abraham never weakened. He was sure that he was doing God's will.

Abraham took with him his wife, Sarah, and his nephew, Lot, for Abraham had no son at that time. Great herds and flocks and men to take care of them were gathered together. His tents and possessions were packed on the backs of animals. This great company, led by Abraham, started south. All the way to the unknown land, while the company complained and wanted to return to Haran, Abraham listened only to the voice of God.

At last they arrived in the land of Canaan. Abraham built an altar and thanked God for bringing them safely there after the long perilous journey. Then to his joy, he heard God speak to him, saying: "This land on which you stand shall belong to your family in the years to come. You shall be the father of a great nation who shall be a blessing to all the world."

"I don't see how Abraham going to a new country is much like us going to another part of town," said Susan as her father got up to continue preparations for their move.

"Do *you*, Jon?" asked Mr. Grant.

"Well," said Jon thoughtfully. "Abraham was doing what God wanted him to do even though he had to face dangers in the new land. I guess Abraham would meet all kinds of enemies in the new land. He'd have to be brave to go."

"Yes, it took great courage and great trust in God. Going to a new neighbourhood and a new school takes courage and trust too. It is a big change for you and Sue. If we believe that God wants us to make this change because of Gran, then we know he will help us."

After their father had left the room, Susan said, "Maybe moving to Gran's is an adventure God wants us to have. I'll try to believe that it is."

Jon nodded. "It is like an adventure, I guess. One thing I'm glad about. I can come back and visit Chuck Duncan on Saturdays. We aren't going as far as Abraham did, from Haran to the land of Canaan. We're just changing neighbourhoods. It might be fun, after all. Come on. Let's start packing!"

chapter 10

CHOOSING THE BEST

"I want the big bedroom with the balcony!" shouted Jon as he and Susan rushed into Gran's house.

"I said I wanted it first!" Susan let out a wail because Jon was already up the stairs ahead of her. "Mother, stop him!"

Mrs. Grant hurried upstairs after them. "Children, I'm ashamed of you! Gran may be sleeping. Don't be so noisy!"

"But Mother!" Susan whispered fiercely. "It isn't fair!

Jon's chosen the best bedroom." She pointed to the closed door. "He's in there now, and he won't open up!"

Mrs. Grant tapped quickly on the door. Soon Jon's head appeared. "Count to nine! It's mine! First come! First served!" he chanted grinning.

"Sh!" Mrs. Grant looked disturbed. "We should have decided which bedrooms you'd have before we moved. I've been so busy the thought never occurred to me."

"Hello everybody! Welcome home!" It was Gran calling from down the hall. Soon the Grants were in her room apologizing for making so much noise.

"It isn't every day that my family moves in with me!" said Gran smiling at each one of them. "I'm so happy to have you here that I can put up with a bit of noise."

"Gran, may I have the bedroom with the balcony?" asked Susan in a coaxing voice. "That's the one I want."

"That's the one I've got!" announced Jon.

Gran and Mrs. Grant looked at each other. Then Gran said, "Jon and Susan, you stay with me until we decide what's to be done. Your mother has too many immediate things to see to right now. Let's not bother her."

"Thank you, Gran!" Mrs. Grant gave a sigh of relief. "Now be good children and have a nice visit with Gran while your father and I go back to the other house for our clothing."

"This bedroom business *is* a problem," said Gran after Mr. and Mrs. Grant left. "I want you both to be happy here in this home. There's a very nice bedroom for one of you along the other side of the hall."

"It hasn't a balcony," said Jon, his grin fading.

"No, it hasn't." Gran looked first at him and then at Susan.

44

"Dear me, how do we settle matters like this?"

Jon and Susan were silent. They looked angrily at each other. "Don't your mother and father try to think of a Bible story that will give you an answer?"

"Oh Gran!" Susan shook her head. "How could a Bible story tell Jon he should let me have that balcony bedroom?"

"Gran might know a story that would tell *you* to let *me* have it," retorted Jon.

"Why, I do believe I've thought of just the right story!" Gran looked pleased. "And it is about Abraham too."

"You mean there are more stories about Abraham?" asked Jon.

"Yes," said Gran. "This one is about Abraham and his nephew, Lot."

"Tell us the story, please, Gran," said Susan.

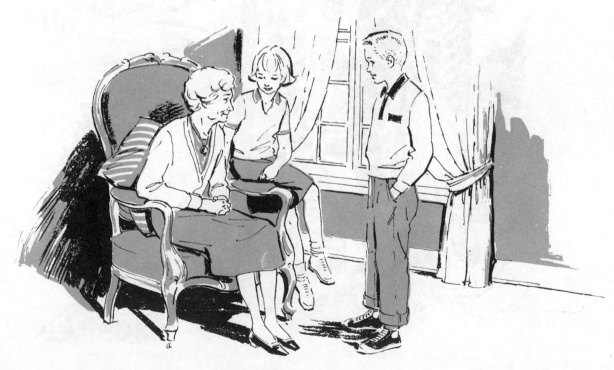

Abraham Gives Lot First Choice

It was early evening. Abraham sat in front of his tent and watched his herdsmen come up from the valleys bringing the cattle to be watered at the well. From the opposite direction came the herdsmen of Lot. They were pushing the cattle forward trying to reach the well first.

What was wrong? The men looked angry. Abraham stood up and watched as the herdsmen came together and argued violently.

"We are here first!" cried Lot's men. "Let our cattle drink first!"

"You took our grazing fields today!" came the reply. "Abraham is the leader of our caravan. The herds and flocks of Lot can wait."

The quarrelling continued until the men saw that Abraham was watching. Muttering to themselves, Lot's men stood back and let the others water the animals.

"There must be no quarrelling between Lot and me," said Abraham to his wife Sarah. "We had best separate. This land is large and plentiful. There is enough for us all. I shall tell him so tomorrow."

"Be careful that he doesn't trick you into giving him the best grazing land," said Sarah.

Abraham smiled. "God has been good to us. This is a land of plenty whichever way we turn."

The next day Abraham and Lot went up on the highest hill

to look over the land. Lot's heart beat fast. He knew why they were there and his eyes glistened as he looked down into the rich valley below.

Abraham said to him, "There must be no quarrelling or anger between my herdsmen and your herdsmen. I am your uncle, you are my nephew. We belong to the same family."

Lot spoke not a word. He waited, his eyes on the land below

Abraham smiled. "You may choose where you will graze your herds and flocks. Choose the wells that your herdsmen and shepherds will use. I will go to the left if you choose the right. If you choose the left I will go right. There is enough for us all if we dwell apart."

Lot looked down at the Jordan Valley that was well-watered and green. He spoke quickly as if afraid that his uncle would change his mind.

"I choose the Jordan Valley!"

And so Abraham went down to his wife who waited for him and told her they would move into the eastern hills.

Sarah could not understand why Abraham, the stronger and greater man, had let selfish young Lot choose the best land.

But Abraham was content. He had done what he felt God would want him to do. He had kept peace between himself and Lot.

"I like the way you tell stories, Gran." Susan gave her a hug. "And Jon, just because I'm younger like Lot, I don't have to be greedy like him. I'm going to be nice like Abraham and let you have the balcony bedroom."

"Well, you don't have to act as if you were doing me a great big favour. I'm the older, so I'm supposed to let you have it."

"Dear, dear!" Gran laughed. "If you are both trying to be nice, I wouldn't know it by your voices! You both still want that bedroom, don't you? It's hard to give up the balcony. Is there any other reason why one of you should have that particular room?"

There was a long silence. Then Susan gave a sigh.

"Jon is bigger than I am. He should have the bigger room, maybe. He has more stuff to put in it, and he does more home-work. There's a big desk in that room."

Jon grinned and shook his head. "Thanks, but I can get along all right in the other room. I just remembered that you have nightmares sometimes. The balcony bedroom is beside the one Mother and Dad have. You should be close to them so they can hear you. I don't want you getting scared at night."

"Oh." Susan didn't know what else to say. "Well, maybe I'll get over the nightmares soon and we can trade bedrooms later."

"Okay!" Jon turned to Gran. "I'm hungry, Gran. Can we make a snack for us all?"

"A good idea! There are cookies and milk in the fridge. Let's have a moving-in snack right here. Use the tray on top of the sideboard. I'll be ready for you by the time you get back!"

chapter 11

May/82

THE COURAGE TO BE KIND

"Mother!" called Susan as she rushed into the house one late fall afternoon. "I know who's been stealing Gran's flowers. It's Betty and Nora Craner down the street!"

"Are you sure?" Mrs. Grant had missed the chrysanthemums. She liked to have them for Gran's room.

"Yes, I'm sure. They . . ."

A call from Gran's bedroom interrupted them.

"So little Betty and Nora Craner are taking our flowers," said Gran, when Mrs. Grant and Susan told her. "Do you know what they do with them, Susan?"

"Yes, Gran! They give them to our teacher, Miss Best. And Miss Best makes such a fuss over them. It isn't fair!"

"Did you tell Miss Best where the flowers came from?"

"No, I don't talk to Miss Best very much yet."

"It's strange for you in a new school, I know, Dear." Gran smiled. "But I'm glad you didn't tell Miss Best."

"But they were stealing, Gran!"

"Well, Susan, I used to give them flowers last spring to take to school. They haven't a garden of their own. I don't suppose they think of it as stealing."

"They sneaked into our garden as if they did! Gran, I should be taking the flowers to Miss Best, but Mother thinks we should save them for you, so I haven't."

Mrs. Grant rose. "I'll leave you together while I finish the ironing. Perhaps Gran can think of a Bible story that will help us see what we should do."

"I already know what to do!" said Susan. "We should stop Nora and Betty from stealing!"

"You don't want a story?" asked Gran.

"Oh, I guess so." Susan settled down at the foot of the bed. So Gran told this story.

Isaac and the Wells

For many years Abraham and his wife Sarah had no children. At last to their wonder and delight a little son was born to them.

"Because he has filled our lives with joy and laughter," said Sarah, "we will call him Isaac."

Isaac grew into a fine boy. His parents were proud of him. Abraham's heart was thankful every time he looked at his son.

"God has kept his promise to me," he would say to himself. "He promised that my family would be a great nation. Now I have a son to become a leader. After I am no longer here, Isaac will follow in my footsteps."

And it was so. When Abraham died, Isaac became chief of the tribe. The tribe grew in riches and in strength as it travelled throughout the land of Canaan in search of grazing land and water.

Water in the dry places of the world is very precious Many wells had been dug by Abraham years before, but other tribes had filled them up with rocks.

One day Isaac's men cleaned out one of the old wells as they searched for water. To their joy, fresh water came bubbling up

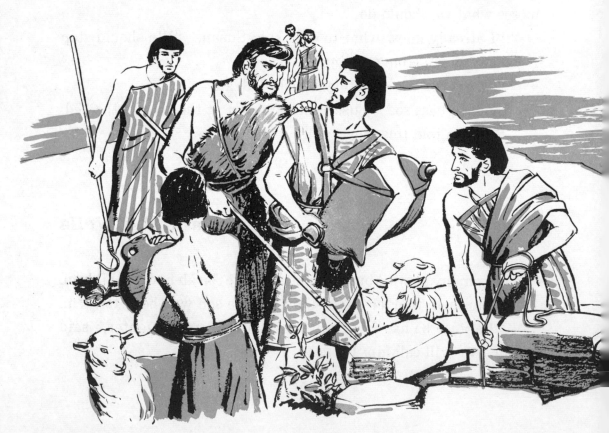

from within. The good news spread and soon the shepherds and herdsmen of Isaac's tribe gathered to water their animals.

Suddenly shepherds from another tribe rushed down from the hills.

"This well is ours!" they cried. And they forced Isaac's men to leave.

Isaac's men wanted to fight, but he said, "Let us move on and find another well."

This they did, but again the men of another tribe came forward and drove them away. The shepherds and herdsmen of Isaac were angry and ready to fight, but again Isaac told them to turn away and search for water elsewhere.

This happened again and again. Isaac's men could not understand why they were forbidden to fight. At last, however, the tribe dug a well from which came fresh cool water and this time there was no quarrel. Men and animals had all the water they wished to drink.

"The Lord has made room for us," said Isaac and he was pleased. He had kept his tribe from fighting with others and now

they could live in peace with their neighbours as his father, Abraham, would want them to do. His neighbours had discovered that Isaac came among them in peace.

And so Isaac worshipped the God of his father and God blessed him with the promise that he would be with him always.

"I think it's hard not to get cross when people do mean things," said Susan when her grandmother finished the story. "Isaac was very easy-going, wasn't he?"

"No, Isaac was a very strong person. It would have been easier to fight back. The world is made a happier place by men like Isaac who have strength to understand people."

"I guess you want me to let Nora and Betty keep taking our flowers to Miss Best," Susan sighed.

"In this situation I think it would be the right thing to do. But can you think of some way of helping them feel better about taking the flowers?"

"Maybe if I invited them in to pick the flowers it would be better, but Gran, I want to take some to Miss Best, too."

"Of course!" Gran laughed. "There were enough wells for Isaac and his neighbours, I think there are enough flowers for us all, too, if we manage properly. And if you and Nora and Betty take flowers together to Miss Best, you'll all get better acquainted, won't you?"

"Why, yes, we will! Gran, I must remember this story about Isaac to tell Jon. I wonder if he has heard it."

You might like to read from your Bible:

Matthew 5: 43-48 (We are to love our enemies)

54

chapter 12

LIVING ON THE OUTSIDE

Something was wrong with Jon. He quarrelled with Bill Becker after school. He grumbled about helping his father shovel away the first snow of the season. He made Susan cry by pushing her out of his favourite chair in the living room.

"Jon, what *is* the matter with you?" asked his mother. "Usually you are so pleasant to live with."

"Nothing's the matter," muttered Jon as he got up and let Susan sit down again. He flung himself on the floor and tried to read a book. He didn't really know what was wrong with him. He guessed he was just feeling mean and his friends and family didn't make him feel any better either.

After supper, Susan asked for a story.

"Mother says Isaac had twin boys, Daddy. Tell me about them, please."

Mr. Grant smiled. "The story of Esau and Jacob was one of my favourite stories when I was your age. I'll tell you the first part of it tonight." He raised his voice. "Jon! Are you finished with your homework? Do you want to hear a story?"

Jon came slowly into the room. He had been through with his homework for some time. Without saying anything, he sat down near by.

Mr. Grant began:

Jacob and Esau

Isaac, the son of Abraham was old and almost blind but he had two sons to take over the leadership and care of his great tribe.

His sons were twins. Jacob was the younger by only a few minutes and he was the smarter of the two boys. Esau was red-haired and strong. Isaac was proud of both boys, but Esau would become head of the tribe because he was older and so Isaac spent much time with him hoping to train him to lead the people wisely and well.

Jacob was jealous. He grumbled to his mother, and she took his part for Jacob was her favourite son.

One day the old father called to Esau and said, "My son, take your bow and arrow and go out to the field and hunt game for me. Cook me a good meal of it and then I will give you my blessing before I die."

Rebekah, the mother, heard these words and as soon as Esau left, she called Jacob to her and told him what his father had said.

"My son," she said, "you shall have your father's blessing instead of Esau so that you may become leader of our people. Obey me now. Go to the flocks and bring back two young goats that I may make a savoury stew for your father. You shall take it to him to eat. Then he will bless you before he dies."

"But," said Jacob, "I am not strong and hairy like Esau. My father will feel my arms and know me as Jacob."

"You shall wear Esau's clothes and I will put hairy goat skins on your arms and neck. Then if your father should touch you he will think you are Esau."

56

Jacob did as his mother told him. With the dish of stew in his hands and the coat of skins on his arms he went into Isaac's tent.

"Who are you?" asked the old man holding out his hands.

"I am your first-born son, Esau," said Jacob in a deep voice, "and I have brought you savoury meat that you may eat and give me your blessing."

"Come near me, my son. The voice seems to be the voice of Jacob." Then he felt his son's arms. "But these are Esau's hairy arms." So the old father was satisfied. He dined upon the meat that had been brought. Then he placed his hands on Jacob's head and blessed him, saying: "Let people serve you and nations bow down to you. Be lord over your brother."

Jacob hurried away just in time. Esau had returned from his hunt.

"Who are you?" asked Isaac hearing footsteps.

"I am Esau, your first-born son. I have brought you some savoury meat.so that you may eat it and then give me your blessing."

The old father began to tremble. "Who was it came before you? Who brought me meat and received my blessing?"

Then Esau knew he had been tricked by his brother. He left his father's tent with deep anger in his heart. He made up his mind to do great harm to Jacob.

Jacob, frightened at what his selfishness had done to keep him away from his father and brother, now decided to run from home, out into the wilderness.

"Oh Daddy, what happened next?" asked Susan as her father stopped.

"I'll tell you some more tomorrow evening. Now it is time for you to go to bed."

After Susan and Mrs. Grant went upstairs, Jon sat in silence for a long time.

"Tell me what's troubling you, Son," said Mr. Grant at last.

Jon started to speak, stopped, and then started again.

"Dad, I did something mean yesterday at school."

His father waited.

"I . . . Dad, you know Luis Bonito. He's the one in school who's so smart and is always trying to beat me in everything. It's between him and me who stands first. Well, yesterday was the deadline for our report on WINTER HOMES OF ANIMALS. I . . . " Jon's face turned red with misery. "Dad, Luis dropped his report in the school yard and I found it. Well . . . I handed my report in, but I hid Luis's paper. I still have it upstairs."

"What did Luis say to your teacher?" asked Mr. Grant looking grave.

"Oh, he was almost crying. He is always so cocky about his work. At first I got a kick out of seeing him like that, but since

then I've been feeling sort of sick. I'm sorry, Dad," Jon turned his head away. "I didn't know what was making me mean, but when I heard you tell what Jacob did, I knew all of a sudden why I was feeling bad and was so crabby."

"You felt as if you were on the outside—not good friends with any of us?" His father's voice was quiet.

"I guess so. I didn't feel like being nice to any one."

"Jacob discovered something like that too, Jon. It was as if he had moved away from God. We leave God out of our lives when we are selfish."

There was a silence.

"What should I do to fix things up, Dad?" asked Jon at last.

"What do you think you should do?"

"I could put Luis's report on Mr. Barnes' desk."

"But won't marks be taken off because it is two days late?"

Jon nodded slowly. "But do I have to tell Mr. Barnes what I did?"

Mr. Grant went over and put his arm around Jon's shoulder. He did not need to answer the question. Jon understood.

"It'll be real hard to do that, Dad. Mr. Barnes will think I'm an awful guy. So will Luis."

"How will you feel towards God if you do this hard thing?" asked Mr. Grant smiling.

Jon stood up with a big sigh.

"I sure wish tomorrow were over. But I'm glad I told you, Dad. I feel better already."

To his surprise Jon found himself whistling softly as he went upstairs to bed.

chapter 13

Feb 6/82

GOD'S CONSTANT LOVE

Jon and Susan had not meant to disobey their father, but the fire-engine careening down the street made them forget the promise they had made to stay at home while Mr. and Mrs. Grant did some shopping. Gran might need them, so they were to stay within call.

At the sight of their friends joining the gathering crowd, Susan and Jon rushed down the streets with them and watched as a corner store went up in flames. How long they were there, they did not know, but suddenly Jon caught Susan by the arm.

"We'd better get home! We forgot that we were to stay with Gran while Mother and Dad went shopping!"

"Oh Jon!" Susan began to cry as they raced for home. "What if something's happened to Gran! What will Mother and Daddy do to us?"

When they arrived home Mr. and Mrs. Grant were looking for them. There was a long talk about disobedience and there was a punishment. No television for three days!

That evening as they sat in the living room, reading, Susan and Jon were happy again. Their father had just joked with them and their mother had brought in some popcorn from the kitchen.

"You aren't angry with us any more, are you Mother?" said Susan as she took a handful of popcorn.

"No, I am not angry with you Susan. Daddy and I certainly were disappointed with you this afternoon. We had trusted you, and you had failed us."

"You'd never stop loving us no matter what we did, would you?" asked Susan. Jon looked up.

"We'll always love you. Be sure of that. Sometimes, however, our love is hurt. And sometimes our love has to forgive a great deal."

"Blind Isaac in the Bible trusted Jacob and he did far worse things than Jon and I did. Did Isaac forgive Jacob?"

"Yes and he gave Jacob another blessing meant especially for him."

"But did God forgive Jacob for lying to his father and for stealing from his brother?" asked Jon.

Mr. Grant reached for the Bible on a nearby table. "I think we can find out by reading the second story about Jacob. Rebekah was afraid Esau might harm Jacob, so she told him to run away from home and go to her homeland where her brother Laban would keep him. When it was safe for Jacob to return, she would let him know. Here is the story in Genesis 28, verses 10 to 22. Let us read it straight from the Bible.

"Jacob left Beersheba, and went toward Haran.
And he came to a certain place, and stayed there that
night, because the sun had set. Taking one of the
stones of the place, he put it under his head and lay
down in that place to sleep. And he dreamed that
there was a ladder set up on the earth, and the top of
it reached to heaven; and behold, the angels of God
were ascending and descending on it! And behold,
the Lord stood above it and said, 'I am the Lord, the
God of Abraham your father and the God of Isaac;

the land on which you lie I will give to you and to your descendants; and your descendants shall be like the dust of the earth, and you shall spread abroad to the west and to the east and to the north and to the south; and by you and your descendants shall all the families of the earth bless themselves. Behold, I am with you and will keep you wherever you go, and will bring you back to this land; for I will not leave you until I have done that of which I have spoken to you.' Then

Jacob awoke from his sleep and said, 'Surely the Lord is in this place; and I did not know it.' And he was afraid, and said, 'How awesome is this place! This is none other than the house of God, and this is the gate of heaven.'

"So Jacob rose early in the morning, and he took the stone which he had put under his head and set it up for a pillar and poured oil on the top of it. He called the name of that place Bethel; but the name of the city was Luz at the first. Then Jacob made a vow, saying, 'If God will be with me, and will keep me in this way that I go, and will give me bread to eat and clothing to wear, so that I come again to my father's house in peace, then the Lord shall be my God, and this stone, which I have set up for a pillar, shall be God's house; and of all that thou givest me I will give the tenth to thee.' "

"Oh, I'm glad God still loved Jacob," said Susan when the story was finished. "While you were reading, Daddy, I felt awfully sorry for Jacob. I was afraid for him."

"I'm glad to know that God forgives people when they do wrong," said Jon reaching for more popcorn.

"Because God loves and forgives us, we should try to be better day by day," said Mrs. Grant. "We wouldn't want to go on hurting his love day after day any more than you would want to go on disappointing us."

"Mother, I'm beginning to really love God," said Susan after a short silence. "I'm so glad he cares for us."

Her mother nodded. "I think that was the way Jacob felt after his dream. He was filled with joy because he knew that God was still with him and would never leave him. And when you feel that way about God you never want to hurt him again."

You might like to read from your Bible:

1 Corinthians 13 (A hymn that describes the amazing love of God)

chapter 14

A JOYFUL HOMECOMING

"What happened to Jacob after he ran away from home?" asked Jon of his father one evening.

"Did he and Esau ever make up?" Susan, who was drawing at the dining room table, left her pastel crayons and joined Jon on the living room rug.

"Jacob learned what it was like to be tricked," Mr. Grant told them. "Uncle Laban was dishonest with him, but I'm sorry to say it was many years before Jacob himself learned to be honest and be sorry for his misdeeds."

"Tell us, Daddy!" Susan reached for a footstool and put it under her father's feet. Mr. Grant settled back in his easy chair.

"Thanks Sue. I might as well get comfortable for this is a long story."

"Jacob's story was one of my favourites when I was young. It was a real life adventure," said Mrs. Grant as she came into the room and sat down. "I want to hear it again, too!"

Jacob and Laban

After Jacob woke from his dream and knew that God was still with him, he journeyed on with a lighter heart. Travelling for

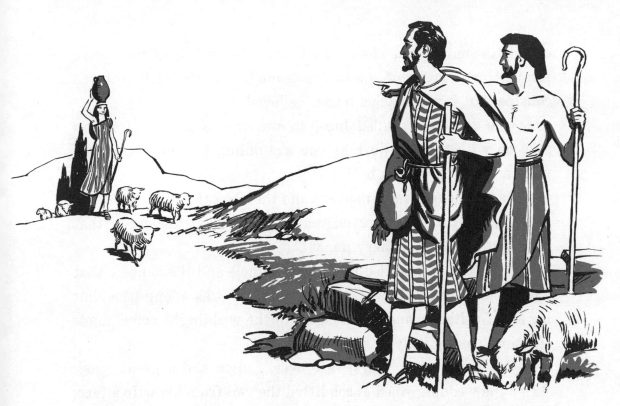

many miles, he finally came to a pleasant land of green fields and pastures.

"Do you know Laban, the son of Nahor?" Jacob asked some shepherds who were waiting near a well to water their flocks.

"Yes, we know him," said the shepherds. "And look, there is Rachel, his daughter, coming to the well with her sheep."

Eagerly Jacob turned to watch his cousin leading her flocks across the fields. She was a beautiful girl and when Jacob ran forward to tell her who he was, he found that she was kind and friendly too. Together they watered the sheep and then went back to her father's house. Laban came out and was pleased to see Jacob, his sister's son. He welcomed him into the family circle and invited him to remain.

Several weeks went by and Jacob lived happily with his uncle. There were two daughters of Laban. The younger was called Rachel and the older was Leah. As he helped them care for the large flocks of sheep, Jacob made friends with both his cousins, but it was Rachel whom he loved.

One day Laban called Jacob to him and said, "Jacob, if you stay on with me and work as you are doing, I want to pay you wages. What will they be?"

Jacob thought for a moment and then he said, "I do not want a wage, but I will work seven years for you if at the end of that time you will let me marry Rachel."

And so it was settled between the uncle and the nephew that Jacob should stay and work seven years. It was a long time, but his love for Rachel and the thoughts of the wedding to come, made the time pass quickly.

When the seven years were over, Laban had a great feast. After the wedding when Jacob lifted the veil from his wife's face, he discovered that his uncle had tricked him. Instead of Rachel, it was Leah, the older sister, whom he had married.

"Why did you deceive me?" Jacob cried out in anger to his uncle. "Seven years have I worked for Rachel and you give me Leah instead!"

"It is right that the elder daughter be married first," said Laban. "If you work another seven years for me then I will give you Rachel as well."

As it was the custom in those days for a man to have more than one wife, there was nothing that Jacob could do but agree. He loved Rachel too well not to do it.

The next seven years were much longer than the first seven. Jacob learned what it was like to be treated unfairly. He who had tricked his father and brother was now being tricked by his uncle. But Jacob was still dishonest too. As the years passed, he tricked Laban, his uncle, in many ways and so became rich.

Laban and his sons grew to dislike and fear Jacob. Twenty years later Jacob knew he must leave if he wanted to save himself from their anger. He was now a wealthy man with many children. He wanted to return to his home in the land of Canaan.

Without saying good-bye to Laban, he set forth leading a great company. Leah and Rachel, with eleven sons and one daughter, rode on camels behind him. Flocks of sheep and herds of cattle, herdsmen, shepherds, men and women servants followed on foot.

After Jacob had gone, Laban discovered that many of his animals and household possessions were missing. He and his sons chased after Jacob and caught up with them. Bitter words were

spoken. Laban accused Jacob of trickery. Jacob accused Laban of the same. At last, because Laban loved his daughters and their children, he let Jacob travel on, but he threatened him still with what he would do if his daughters and grandchildren were not treated fairly.

You can imagine how lucky Jacob felt to be free to go on his journey. But even so, he had a great deal to think about as he neared his old home. What would Esau do when they met? Would he still be angry with him for having stolen his birthright? Would he ride forth with a company of men and kill Jacob and his children and steal his cattle?

Jacob sent a messenger ahead to tell Esau of his arrival. The messenger was to tell Esau of the many gifts that Jacob was bringing to him.

Yet Jacob knew that if Esau wished he could take everything without asking because he would be the stronger with more fighting men on his side.

The night before he was to meet Esau, Jacob prayed to God that the reunion with his brother would be peaceful and happy. This was not enough. Jacob had to examine his own heart and realize that he had been a wicked man for many years. In the deep of the night, he thought of God and wondered what God thought of him. It seemed that he wrestled all night long with these thoughts until he realized that he must be different if he were to be a servant of God. In the morning he arose a new man, pledged to conquer his pride and self-will.

With fast-beating heart he rode out to meet Esau and the large company of men. To his great joy, Esau's anger was gone. The older brother threw his arms around Jacob and kissed him. Then he welcomed Leah and Rachel and all the children. It was an exciting and happy homecoming for Jacob.

And so Jacob made a home for himself and his family in the land of Canaan; the land which God had promised to give his children.

Susan gave a big satisfied sigh.

"Mother, the story of Jacob and Rachel is going to be one of my favourite Bible stories too. I'm glad Jacob married Rachel and made up with Esau."

Jon agreed. "It's a keen story, Dad. I wish it had been longer."

chapter 15

WHY WE HAVE CHRISTMAS

It was Christmas Eve.

The Grants had just finished decorating a lovely fir-tree in one corner of the living room. Now Mr. Grant came down the stairs carrying Gran. Mrs. Grant followed with gay pillows and blankets.

Susan rushed forward to clear away the empty decoration boxes from the couch, and Jon threw some cones on the fire that gave out a cheerful crackle and a bright blue flame.

Betty and Nora Craner, Bill Becker, and Carol Moto watched the Grants as they got Gran comfortably settled.

The Grants had intended spending Christmas Eve alone, but when Mr. and Mrs. Becker asked if Bill could stay with them because they had to go out, the Grants had warmly welcomed him. Susan wanted a friend too.

"Mother, may I ask Carol Moto to come in for a while? Carol's new on our street and I remember how that feels!"

"May we have our friends, Betty and Nora Craner?" asked Gran, smiling.

Mrs. Grant looked at Susan who nodded slowly. She still didn't approve entirely of Nora and Betty. They were untidy. Their hair always seemed to need brushing and their clothes were not always clean.

So Christmas Eve at the Grants became a party.

After Gran was comfortable, the tree lights were put on and Mrs. Grant and Susan passed around ice-cream and Christmas cookies.

"What do we do now?" asked Betty Craner, her brown eyes looking from one face to another.

"Well, we've decorated the tree and played games. What else is there to do?" asked Bill who was finishing his second dish of ice cream.

"Dad always reads us the Christmas story on this night," said Jon. "We can hear that before you go home, if you like."

"Okay," said Bill. "I haven't had a story read to me for a long time."

"I like to hear stories," said Carol Moto as she carefully brushed some cooky crumbs into her paper napkin. "Japanese fairy stories are my favourite ones."

Mr. Grant nodded. "We can learn a good deal from some stories, can't we? Jon and Susan read by themselves now, so most of the stories that we tell to them are from the Bible."

"The Bible is hard to read, isn't it?"

"Some parts of the Bible are hard to understand, but we have found out that many people in the Bible had troubles something like the ones we have today, so we try to find out what they did about them."

"We've been hearing about Abraham, Isaac, and Jacob," said Jon to Bill. "They were nomads and lived mostly in tents and moved whenever their animals needed better grazing land."

"And they wanted to know what God was like," said Susan.

"How did they find out?" asked Betty, as she moved away from the heat of the fire.

"They listened to God's voice," Susan told her. "It ... Daddy, you tell us."

Mr. Grant picked up the Bible. "The first part of the Bible tells us about Abraham and his sons and grandsons and the people who followed them. These people seemed to understand God's plan for them better than any other people in those days, thousands of years ago. They became a great nation, but it was not always easy for them to do what was right. They quarrelled and fought among themselves. They did not obey God's laws. They did not always listen to God's voice."

"God knew that the people still did not understand him. They did not carry out the plans he had for them," said Gran. "And so God decided to send his son, Jesus, into the world to show the people what his love was really like and what he really wanted people to be like."

"Oh," said Nora, surprised. "Is that why Christmas is so important? I thought it was just to give and to get presents, and to have a good time."

"We give presents and have a happy time on Christmas because we are glad that Jesus was born into the world. We want to celebrate his birthday."

"Tell us the Christmas story, Daddy!" said Susan.

"I'm going to read it, Susan, and from the Gospel According to Luke," said Mr. Grant. "It is in chapter 2, verses 1 to 20."

The First Christmas

"In those days a decree went out from Caesar Augustus that all the world should be enrolled. This was the first enrolment, when Quirinius was governor of Syria. And all went to be enrolled, each to his own city. And Joseph also went up from Galilee, from the city of Nazareth, to Judea, to the city of David, which is called Bethlehem, because he was of the house and lineage of David, to be enrolled with Mary, his betrothed, who was with child. And while they were there, the time came for her to be delivered. And she gave birth to her first-born son and wrapped him in swaddling cloths, and laid him in a manger, because there was no place for them in the inn.

"And in that region there were shepherds out in the field, keeping watch over their flock by night. And an angel of the Lord appeared to them, and the glory of the Lord shone around them, and they were filled with fear. And the angel said to them, 'Be not afraid; for behold, I bring you good news of a great joy which will come to all the people; for to you is born this day in the city of David a Saviour, who is Christ the Lord. And this will be a sign for you: you will find a babe wrapped in swaddling cloths and lying in a manger.' And suddenly there was with the angel a multitude of the heavenly host praising God and saying, 'Glory to God in the highest, and on earth peace among men with whom he is pleased!'

"When the angels went away from them into heaven, the shepherds said to one another, 'Let us go over to Bethlehem and see this thing that has happened which the Lord has made known to us.' And they went with haste, and found Mary and Joseph, and the babe lying in a manger. And when they saw it they made known the saying which had been told them concerning this child; and all who heard it wondered at what the shepherds told them. But Mary kept all these things, pondering them in her heart. And the shepherds returned, glorifying and praising God for all they had heard and seen, as it had been told them."

Mr. Grant closed the Bible saying, "And when the baby Jesus was a week old, Mary and Joseph took him to the temple in Jerusalem. Simeon, a man of God, held the baby in his arms, praised God and blessed Mary, Joseph and the baby. Mary and Joseph then took Jesus home where he grew and became·strong, and increased in wisdom; and the favour of God was upon him."

"This is one of the best Christmas Eve's I've ever had," said Bill Becker. "Always before I thought it went too slow."

Gran was pulling coloured strings out from under her blankets. On the end of each one was a name.

"Merry Christmas, everybody!" she said, "Find your name and pull the string!"

There was a string for everyone, even for Mr. and Mrs.

Grant. Everybody pulled and out from under the blankets came Christmas wrapped parcels.

"How did you get them in there without us seeing?" asked Susan, but she didn't wait for an answer, as she and her friends opened their presents.

"Mittens! With bells on them!" said Nora.

"Mine have soft pom-poms!" said Carol. "Thank you, Mrs. Grant."

"So have mine!" Susan gave her grandmother a hug.

"Mine have bells like Nora's! Thanks a lot!" Betty put on her mittens and made them jingle.

Bill's mittens had long cuffs and pictures of hockey players knitted into them. So had Jon's. Both boys were pleased.

"Can we sing a Christmas hymn before we go home?" asked Carol. "My favourite is 'O little town of Bethlehem.' "

"A carol for Carol!" said Jon and started the singing.

After their friends had left, Jon looked at his grandmother and said, "Gran, coming to live with you has been a real adventure. I'm so glad we came!"

"Oh yes!" agreed Susan. "This is *home!*"

chapter 16

GOD NEVER LOSES US

"What did you do in Sunday church school today, Sue?" asked Mr. Grant as the family began lunch after returning from church.

"Oh, it was fun! I like the different ways we learn in this Sunday school." Susan's blue eyes sparkled. "We put on a play this morning about one of the stories Jesus told. I was a woman who only had ten pieces of money to take care of her large family. I was very upset when I lost a coin. Betty was supposed to be my neighbour. She said, 'Don't worry, you have nine other pieces of money.'

"But I shook my head, took my lamp and got out my broom. I swept and swept into every corner until at last I found my lost money."

"That story is called, 'The Lost Coin,'" said Mrs. Grant as she passed the salad to Jon. "What did you do when you found your coin, Susan?"

"Well," Susan took a deep breath. "I found it under some books in a corner. The books were supposed to be big jars. When I found it, I called in all my neighbours and told them. Then we celebrated together."

"How did you celebrate?" asked Jon.

79

"We laughed and hugged one another and then I served some cookies—just pretend!"

Jon looked puzzled. "Whatever does that story mean?" he asked.

"I know!" Susan said quickly. "Jesus told this story to show that no matter how many good people God has close to him, if one of us does something wrong and moves away from him and gets lost, God searches for us and is glad when he finds us."

"Oh," said Jon. "There's another story about getting lost, isn't there, Dad?—'The Lost Sheep'?"

"Yes, it's also called, 'The Good Shepherd,' and is one of the best known stories that Jesus told. It means very much the same as 'The Lost Coin.'"

"Tell us the story, Daddy," said Susan.

Her father smiled. "I hope I can tell it as well as you told your story, Sue. Yours was very interesting."

The Lost Sheep

In the days of Jesus many shepherds roamed with their sheep over the hills and into the valleys of Galilee in search of water and green grass. Each sheep knew its own shepherd's voice and all through the day the shepherds could be heard calling their sheep together. At night they usually led their sheep into a sheep-fold on the hillside. The sheep-fold was made of four rough stone walls which protected the sheep from the wild animals that came out at night in search of food.

One evening a good shepherd stood at the sheep-fold gate counting his sheep as they entered. He was looking forward to a rest with his friends by the camp-fire, for the night was growing cold and dark. No stars could be seen in the sky and a wind was blowing up a storm.

One by one he counted the sheep and the lambs. "Ninety-seven, ninety-eight, ninety-nine . . ."

One sheep was missing! The shepherd knew that he had counted correctly and he knew that there should be one hundred sheep in the fold.

He looked out at the dark hills and he drew his cloak closer about his shoulders as the wild wind blew. Closing the gate so his ninety and nine would be safe, he took up his long crook and strode off into the darkness to search for his one lost sheep.

Along winding paths and into the rocky hills, he went. His voice rose and fell with the wind as he called the sheep by name. There was no answer.

Had a wolf already found the sheep? The good shepherd hurried on into a deep ravine. Again and again he called his lost sheep, hoping to hear an answer.

As he passed by a stony pit he heard a faint bleating. He stopped and called out. The bleating grew louder.

Eagerly the shepherd climbed down into the pit. Using his crook he reached for the sheep that had been caught between two rocks.

With comforting words the shepherd gathered the sheep in his arms. One of its legs was bruised. Gently the shepherd carried it back to the fold. How glad he was to have found his lost sheep. Now all his flock were safe. When he returned to the camp-fire, he called out to his friends, the other shepherds, and said, "Rejoice with me for I have found my lost sheep."

When his father had finished the story Jon asked, "Dad, how do we get lost from God? Can we really get so lost that even God doesn't know where we are?"

Mr. Grant thought for a moment. Then he said, "No, Jon, I'm sure that God never loses sight of us. The shepherd may sometimes not know where his lost sheep is, but God always knows where we are. But we may lose God. In Jesus' story it was not the shepherd who wandered from the sheep, it was the sheep who wandered away from the shepherd. People may and do wander from God."

"How?" asked a puzzled Susan.

"You might say we lose God when we try to forget God," said Mr. Grant. "We may try not to believe that God is our heavenly Father and that all people everywhere are his children. This means that we forget we belong to a large family where we have a

Father to obey, and brothers and sisters to love and respect. Forgetting God we become selfish or cruel or greedy or rude."

"But we don't have to keep on forgetting God, do we Daddy?" asked Susan.

"No, and Jesus told us why in his stories. When we forget God he doesn't forget us. In fact, he comes after us. When Jesus told the story about the good shepherd going out for his sheep he was really telling us a story about God. And more than that, he was telling a story about himself. For we believe that Jesus is the Good Shepherd. He is God come to earth for the sake of lost people. He has come to show us God and how we should live as people who do know God."

"I never thought about God that way," said Jon slowly. "It's pretty wonderful to know that God never forgets us. I hope I can always remember him."

You might like to read from your Bible:

> *Psalms 23 (God cares for us as a good shepherd cares for his sheep)*

83

chapter 17

Mar/82

IS FORGIVENESS FAIR?

The Grants were having their family worship up in Gran's room. It was her turn to tell the Bible story. She chose another parable told by Jesus:

The Forgiving Father

Once there was a good man who had two sons. The older boy worked with his father and stayed at home, but the younger son longed to get away from home. One day he went to his father

84

and said, "Father, I wish to leave home. Please give me my share of your money now."

The father was sorry to see his son go, but he divided his wealth and away went the young man into a far country.

There he spent his time and money on having fun. Many of the things that he did were wrong, but the young man thought his life was good for he made many new friends and there were many exciting things to do.

In time his money was all spent. Then his new friends would have nothing more to do with him.

The young man was now alone and without money in a foreign land. He went from place to place looking for a way to earn his living. No one needed him. At last a farmer told him he could take care of the pigs.

As a swine-herd, the young man had little food for there was a famine in the land. While he sat minding the pigs, he began to think how foolish he had been. He was so hungry, he would have been glad to eat the pigs' food.

He remembered his father's house.

"Even the servants in my father's home have bread enough to spare while I sit here and starve!" he thought. Then he jumped to his feet as a great longing for home came over him.

"I will go to my father and ask him to forgive me," he thought. "I will tell him I am not worthy to be called his son. I will be glad to be one of his servants."

All the time that his son had been away the father had watched for his return. Every day he went out to look down the road, hoping and longing to see his boy again.

Late one afternoon he saw a tired ragged traveller approaching him. Could this possibly be his son? Indeed, it was! The father ran out to welcome him home.

Even before the son could tell all his story and say how sorry he was, the father welcomed him gladly and forgave all. He took him into the house for rest and a change of clothing. In great joy and excitement the father called out to his household, telling everyone that his son who was lost had been found.

"Bring the best robe and put it on him," he said. "Put a ring on his finger and shoes on his feet. Make ready a feast, let us eat and be merry."

The older son, who had stayed home and helped his father, came in from the fields. When he discovered what was happening, he was jealous and angry. He would not go in to meet his brother nor celebrate his return. He went to his father, grumbling.

"I have worked for you many years. I have obeyed you, but you never once let me have a party so I might have a good time with my friends. Yet look at what you have done for my brother."

"My dear son," said his father, "you are always with me sharing all that I have. You should be glad now, for your brother who did wrong is sorry for it and has returned home. He who was lost is back."

"I don't think it sounds fair," said Jon, when Gran had finished. "The older son had been a better person. He had stayed home to help his dad. Why should his brother have been treated so well?"

Mrs. Grant nodded. "It was hard for me to understand that, too, Jon," she said. "But I know now that Jesus told this story to show us that God's love is for everyone. For the story is a story of how God feels towards us."

"Since it is really a story about God then it isn't unfair at all," piped up Susan. "For we have talked before about God never forgetting anyone."

Gran smiled. "Yes, God never forgets us, no matter who we are. God forgives us all a great deal. Jesus told this story to show us how we all need to be forgiven."

"Oh, Gran," Susan laughed. "You don't ever do anything to be forgiven for!"

Gran shook her head, "Sue, dear, we need God's forgiveness for many, many things. Think about that older brother. He thought he was much better than his younger brother, didn't he? But he must have had many faults too."

"Well, he might have been stuck-up and selfish," Susan agreed.

Gran continued. "The father didn't love the older son just because he did the right things all the time. He must have had to forgive that son for many things, too. That's why he could forgive the younger son so much. For really he loved both sons in the same way."

"I think that's the way it should be," said Jon looking at Susan. "I guess there's no one as fair as God. It's good to know that God doesn't hold things against us when we do wrong."

"We have to be sorry though!" Sue reminded him.

"Sure, and anxious to get back home," added Jon.

"I'm always going to stay close to home," said Susan as she looked round Gran's cosy room.

Jon laughed. "It doesn't mean this kind of home. It means close to God—with God anywhere."

"I know!" Susan told him. "But being close to God is something like being safe and happy, something like the way it is here in Gran's room, only much better."

And as the family looked around the room and at one another they all seemed to agree that Susan might be quite right.

chapter 18

WHAT IS EASTER?

"Isn't Easter supposed to be a happy time?" asked Jon one evening in early April.

"Why, yes," said Mrs. Grant, "for Christians it is the most joyful time of the year."

"But at school recess today, the kids were saying Jesus got killed just before Easter. Bill Becker said the people killed him by putting him on the cross."

"Why did they, Mother?" asked Susan. "How could people kill him when he was so good and kind? It sounds awful to me." Susan shook her head at the thought of it.

"When Jesus was here on earth," answered Mrs. Grant, "there were people who loved him and there were people who disliked him. Jesus had both friends and enemies."

"But how could anyone not like Jesus?" asked Susan again.

"I guess you know that there are times when all of us don't like to hear the truth. Sometimes when we do something wrong we don't like to be reminded of it. And when someone does remind us we can get pretty angry at that person."

Susan nodded her head for she understood what her mother meant.

"And there are times, too," continued Mrs. Grant, "when we don't like to be reminded of the things we haven't done. We promise to do a job for someone or to run an errand for someone,

but we don't keep our promise. It isn't much fun to be found out, is it?"

Susan shook her head.

"It seems to me that Jesus made enemies for himself by both telling the people around him of the wrong things they had done and the good things they hadn't done. Jesus made some people feel very uncomfortable. He taught them that God is the Father of all men and that therefore all men are brothers. He taught the people that they should love their enemies rather than hate them. He taught them that God was able to love and forgive even the worst people. To many people this was good news. It would have been good news to someone who had been told that God no longer cared for him. It would have been good news for someone who had done wrong but was sorry for it. But it must have been bad news to those people who thought God belonged to them alone or who thought they had done their duty when they had helped their friends. It must have been bad news to people who hated their enemies and who couldn't forgive people. What Jesus did was to tell people who pretended they were right that they were really wrong."

"But couldn't God have stopped Jesus' enemies from putting him to death, Mother?" interrupted Susan.

"Yes, I expect that God could have stopped it all, Susan. But I also believe that God knew it was the only way people would come to understand what Jesus meant and that what he said was true. We believe that Jesus died *for us*."

"What does that mean?" asked Jon.

"For me," replied Mrs. Grant, "it means that if people were the way God wanted them to be then they wouldn't want to hurt Jesus at all. If the people Jesus taught had behaved as God's children they would have agreed with what Jesus said. When people killed Jesus they showed what they were really like."

"I think they must have been very bad to do such a thing," said Susan.

"Maybe they didn't know what they were doing," replied Jon.

"And what about ourselves?" asked Mother. "What about us

when we also hurt Jesus?"

"Oh, Mother!" Susan looked shocked. "How could we? Jesus isn't here on earth anymore. Besides, even if he were, I wouldn't hurt him for anything!"

Mrs. Grant thought for a moment. Then she said, "It is true that Jesus isn't here on earth the way he once was, but we do believe that he still lives. His way of life is still the true way and always will be.   We know that we can still hurt Jesus by failing him."

"How?" asked Susan looking puzzled.

"By not loving and living the way Jesus would have us live. It is wrong to feel that we don't like the people who killed Jesus. Jesus loved his enemies and forgave them.   We are not different from the people of Jesus' own day when we find it hard to realize that God is the Father of all people and that we are to love and forgive God's other children. Jesus' death shouldn't make us think only of those who put him on the cross.   Jesus' death should make us think of ourselves."

"But what about Easter, Mother?" asked Jon.   "What has it to do with all this?   Why is Easter the happiest time of the year? All we have talked about is unhappy things, the bad things that people did to Jesus and the bad things we still do."

"Well, Jon, something very wonderful happened after Jesus died. His followers had become frightened and unhappy when they knew that Jesus was going to die. After his death they were all discouraged. They had claimed to love him very much but now thought that perhaps they had made a mistake, that he wasn't really the person they thought he was. He had said that he was God's Son but now he was dead. Then on the third day after he died Jesus was alive again."

"Could they see him? Could they touch him?" Susan's eyes grew big and she spoke excitedly.

"Some of his followers said they did," replied Mrs. Grant. "Just what exactly happened we don't know. But something very exciting certainly happened. Nothing else could have made such a change in the followers of Jesus. After Easter they were suddenly joyful and brave and certain that Jesus was God's Son after

all. They must have really seen Jesus in some way for this to have happened. And it made them believe that God was willing to give them a new life, too. After their failure to really understand Jesus themselves they knew God was willing to forgive them and help them become the people he wanted. And if this was true for them, why not for all people, even the people who had killed Jesus in the first place? So off they went telling people about Jesus' resurrection."

"I guess I understand Easter better," said Jon. "But there is lots that is still hard to understand. Anyway, I'm glad that it is a happy time. It makes me want to be like Jesus as much as I can and to live as God wants me to live."

You might like to read from your Bible:

> *Mark 16: 1-8 (An early account of Jesus' resurrection from the dead)*

chapter 19

WHEN SOMEONE DIES

"The house is so quiet without Gran," said Susan sadly, as she stared out of the window one late afternoon.

Jon looked up from working on his model airplane. He nodded.

"It's a week now since she died, Mother. I can't get used to her not being here. I start to go into her room to tell her something and then I have to stop."

"I miss Gran, too." Mrs. Grant's head was bent over the mending of one of Jon's socks. "I had such pleasant talks with her each day."

"I don't like having people die," said Susan. "I don't like

having Gran leave us. Maybe some day you will die, Mother. You and Daddy!" Susan looked frightened.

Mrs. Grant looked at her. "Daddy and I are healthy and well. I'm sure we have many good years ahead of us. But we all do die some time, Susan."

Jon left the table where he was working and came over to where his mother and Susan were sitting. "Mother," said Jon, "what has happened to Gran? Where is she now? I don't like to think of her out in the cemetery."

"I suppose many people feel that way about cemeteries, Jon," said Mother. "We hear so many queer stories about cemeteries that we get to thinking of them as very cold and unfriendly places. But it really isn't the way Christian people should think. Perhaps we can find the way we should talk about Gran's death. Why don't we begin by talking about memories we have of Gran?" Mrs. Grant put down her mending. "What was there about Gran that we especially liked? Jon, you start."

Jon thought for a moment.

"Gran was always interested in what we did."

"I liked to hear her laugh and sing," said Susan. "And I liked the stories she told us."

"She liked boys," added Jon. "She wasn't always telling me to keep quiet or to watch where I put my feet."

Susan began to speak quickly. "I loved to see Gran do nice things for others—the way she was good to Betty and Nora Craner, and how happy she made old Mrs. McBride by giving her lovely fur coat to her. Gran loved that fur coat. She told me it was Grandpa's last gift to her. But she couldn't wear it when she was ill, and you had one, Mother, and Mrs. McBride did need a warm winter coat!"

Tears came into Mrs. Grant's eyes. "Yes, Gran loved her coat. When Mrs. McBride took it away, Gran cried a little. But soon she was laughing with me about something else."

"Dear Gran!" said Susan. "How I wish she were here!"

Mr. Grant came in at that moment bringing with him a gust of cold air. After he had taken off his coat Susan brought him over to the fire. "Daddy," she said, "tell us what you loved best about Gran."

Mr. Grant's face brightened.

"I love all the memories I have of Gran as my mother. She was so kind and understanding and she always had great trust in me. She expected me to do the right thing. Now, I didn't always do it, but somehow I seemed to get back on the right track more quickly because of Gran and her trust."

"What do you think Gran is doing now?" asked Jon.

"Well, Son, I'm not so sure I really know. I do know that Gran believed that God can be trusted at all times and I do too. I feel that Gran is surrounded by God's love and care. We believe that God's love is with us while we live. I am certain that death doesn't change things as far as God's love is concerned."

"Yes," said Mrs. Grant, "we do have happy memories of Gran's life but the best thing of all is the hope we have in God. For God has told us through Jesus that he has a much more wonderful life for us after we die. This is what Easter means. It is the hope we have when we remember that Jesus rose from the dead. For that reason, too, we shouldn't think of the cemetery as a poor place to have put Gran. Wouldn't Jesus have us think of it more as a garden? When we plant a seed in the ground we bury it. And then a beautiful flower comes up. I like to think of Jesus' resurrection that way. We buried Gran believing that she will rise to the new life God has planned. We can't see that life the way we see flowers in our garden, but we do believe in Jesus as God's risen Son."

There was a long silence. The firelight danced on the quiet faces of the Grant family. Suddenly Susan smiled.

"I'm going to help keep Gran's garden nice this summer. I want to share the flowers with our neighbours just the way Gran shared them."

"I could do something for Mrs. McBride," said Jon thoughtfully. "She sure misses Gran. I could walk her dog for her on bad days."

Mrs. Grant smiled. "You've given me an idea too. I must be sure to have Mrs. McBride drop in to see me often. She will miss her visits with Gran."

Mr. Grant stretched his long legs towards the fire.

———————————

You might like to read from your Bible:

> *John 14: 1-7 (After people die, God gives them a new world to live in)*

chapter 20

THE ACCIDENT

"Did you know that there are baby birds up in your maple tree?" asked Betty Craner of Susan one spring day after school.

Susan stared up at the branches. "How do you know?" she asked. Susan felt she should be the first one to know what was going on in her own garden.

"Oh, there always are!" said Nora. "Every year Betty and I climb up and take a look. That's an easy tree to climb."

Betty said laughing, "I bet Susan's scared to climb up and see."

"She'd be afraid she'd muss her dress," said Nora.

"I wouldn't! I'm not scared."

"Well, then, climb up and see the baby robins!"

"You do it first," said Susan.

Nora laughed. "Anybody's ready to climb up after they see someone else do it. You're scared!"

Susan tightened her lips together and stiffened her shoulders. It was her tree and her yard! Without further words she began to climb.

The branches were low on the trunk and she moved quite

easily from one to another.   Then she came to a high branch where the nest was built.

Nora and Betty urged her on. A robin began to twitter loudly and it flew close to Susan's face.

"That's the father robin!" shouted Betty. "See, Susan, there *are* baby robins in the nest.   The father doesn't want you to go any closer.   But you're almost there!"

It was so exciting that Susan forgot to be afraid. She moved out along the branch, getting nearer and nearer to the nest.   The father bird became more excited too and flew closer to Susan's head.   His wings fanned her cheeks.

In sudden fright Susan let go of the branch to brush him away.

Down she fell onto the grass below!

"Oh, are you hurt?"   Now it was the frightened face of Betty

that came close. She and Nora tried to help Susan up, but her leg was crumpled underneath her body. She let out a sharp cry and fell back upon the grass.

At that moment Mr. Grant drove into the driveway. He hurried over to the girls.

"What happened, Susan?" he asked as he picked her up in his arms.

"My leg, Daddy! It hurts!" Susan began to sob. "It hurts..."

Betty and Nora stood frightened and silent under the tree. They looked at Susan's white face. They looked at Mr. Grant.

Mr. Grant carefully lifted Susan and carried her into the house.

Susan's leg was broken.

"I'm frightened," cried Susan. "Why did God let me break my leg? In my prayers I ask him to take care of me. Every night I ask him. He's supposed to!"

"God doesn't expect us to do foolish things," Mrs. Grant told her, as she washed away the tears with a soft cloth.

Then Susan's mother kissed her. "You made a mistake and are sorry. God will help you get well. Daddy and I will too. And the doctor! Here he comes hurrying up the walk now!"

Susan's lower lip began to tremble. She turned her head and began to cry again.

chapter 21

NEW FRIENDS

"If I'm to help mend this leg," said Dr. Miller, "we had better let Susan visit the hospital for a while."

"I don't want to go to the hospital!" cried Susan. "I've never been there before. I want to stay home."

"The hospital's all right, Sue," said Jon who was standing in the doorway. "I was there overnight when I had my tonsils out. You'll get along fine."

"Of course you will, Dear," said Mrs. Grant as she began to gather some of Susan's night-clothes together. "When I was your age I went to the hospital, and for years after I wanted to be a nurse. I had a good time in the hospital."

"Did they hurt you?"

"They were very gentle with me. I had a few pains after my appendix operation, but they were not nearly as bad as the ones I had before I went in."

"We'll be close to the phone, Susan, and we'll come to see you every day. Remember that the people in the hospital will help you, not hurt you. That is why we have hospitals. That is the way God has planned part of his care for us." Mr. Grant took Susan up in his arms and took her out to the car.

"Good-bye, Sue!" called Jon.

But Susan did not answer. Her eyes were filled with tears and her face was hidden against her father's shoulder.

At the hospital Susan found herself in a clean white bed with two girls looking at her from beds of their own.

"My name is Anne," said the girl with freckles and curly brown hair. "My father is a doctor in this hospital. He can come in and see us whenever he wants to. That's Marie on your other side. Marie came down from the North in a plane. She's a real live Eskimo."

Susan tried not to stare at Marie who had a white cast on her neck and shoulders. Susan had never seen an Eskimo girl before. They smiled at each other.

"What happened to you?" she asked.

Marie's dark eyes were shy. "I fell over a rocky bank and hurt my back. An airplane flew me in to the city."

"I broke my collar-bone," said Anne. "Fell off my bike."

Susan looked down at her leg which was already encased in a cast. She told the girls what had happened to her.

"How come you have to stay in the hospital if your father's a doctor?" she asked Anne suddenly. "I'd have stayed home if I were you."

"Daddy isn't a bone doctor," answered Anne. "Besides, he would tell me that the hospital is the best place to be when you break a bone or get sick."

"Dr. Miller is a good bone doctor," said Marie. "He's fixing me up fine."

Anne nodded. "Daddy says doctors help cure people who are ill and hurt. They help keep people well, too. But it is God who really cures people. Daddy says no one—not even the best doctors in the world—can do that without God's help. I'm going to be a doctor when I grow up. Each one of us has to become responsible for our good health," Anne's voice sounded like a doctor. "My father says that anybody with good sense takes care of his car, but half the time that same person does some awfully silly things in looking after his own body. He forgets to eat the right kind of food, doesn't get enough sleep, or slumps and lounges around without taking exercise. No wonder some people are like worn out cars."

"I think you'll make a good doctor, Anne!" Miss Turner had just come into the room. "And you are right! We have been given good minds to use in the care of our bodies. We should be good stewards and take care of what God has given us."

"What's a steward?" asked Marie.

"I'll look it up," said Anne who had a dictionary, a First Aid book, and an atlas near by. She picked up the dictionary. "L, m, n, o, p, q, r, s," she murmured to herself. "Stew—steward, here it is! 'One who is put in charge of something.'"

"That's us!" said Susan. "Each of us is put in charge of our body."

"Good for you!" said Miss Turner smiling, as she left the room.

"Maybe I'll be a nurse," said Marie shyly, "though once I wanted to be a teacher. But I love Nurse Turner so much! She's good to me. She helps me write letters home. She is my friend.

So is the doctor."

Susan nodded. Both Dr. Miller and Nurse Turner had also been very kind to her.

"Mother says Daddy has love in his fingertips when he operates," Anne told them. "Miss Turner has love in her fingertips too."

Susan decided it was time that she said something.

"I guess God puts the love there," she said. "My mother and father told me that God shows his love for us through the way people help us. I guess we find God's love through the way doctors and nurses help heal us, too. They are friends of us all."

"That's the way it is," agreed Anne. "Would you like to play a game, Susan? We can play, 'I spy with my little eye.' You go first."

Susan's eyes sparkled as she looked around the bright cheerful room.

"I spy with my little eye, something that begins with F!" she said.

Neither Anne nor Marie could guess the answer.

"F for friends!" said Susan looking at them both. And they all laughed together.

You might like to read from your Bible:

> *2 Timothy 2: 1-7 (We all have*
> *to learn to be brave in this life)*

109

chapter 22

SUSAN COMES HOME

"Oh, it's good to be home!" Susan gave a happy sigh as Mrs. Grant made her comfortable on the living room couch. "I only wish I could get back to school right away. I must be far behind the others. And I missed our play in Sunday church school. I was going to help make our scenery. I've missed so many things because of this old broken leg."

"That old broken leg will soon be as good as new," said her mother. "A little more patience, Dear, and you will be back to school and church within a week."

Susan nodded. "My broken leg made good things happen. I made new friends in the hospital. I'll never be afraid of Dr. Miller again. And I hope I see Nurse—Miss Turner often—and Anne and Marie. I'm glad Anne has gone home. I want to have her over here sometime soon to meet my friends. Poor Marie is still in the hospital. I want to phone her and write to her often and think of other things to do for her. She's so far away from home!"

"Good!" said Mrs. Grant. "You mustn't lose your new friends. And speaking of friends, three of them are coming up the front walk right now!"

"Betty, Nora, and Carol!" Susan's eyes shone with excitement. "Oh, Good! Now I can hear what's going on at school!"

Soon the girls were all in the living room having cookies and chocolate milk together. Susan asked questions and her friends answered.

"Yes, the class goldfish are growing!" said Carol Moto.

"There a new girl in our room. Her name is Lucia," Nora told Susan. "She's from Italy and is learning English. We're helping her by playing with her at recess. And she is teaching us some Italian words." Nora looked quite pleased with herself when she said, "*Madre* means mother, *padre* means father, *maestro* means teacher, and *scuolo* means school."

"And *bambola* means doll," put in Carol.

"Miss Best says she'll keep sending you your homework, Susan," said Betty, "just like when you were in the hospital. I told her I'd bring it to you every day after school."

Nora added quickly, "We can play school here and teach you the things we learn every day."

111

"But you always like to play baseball after school, Nora," said Susan.

"Not while you're at home. We want to be with you." Nora and Betty looked at each other. "We're sorry you broke your leg, Susan. We . . . " Nora did not go on. Betty started to speak quickly.

"We'll be your legs for you this week. We promise. Anything you want us to do—we'll do it!"

Susan was pleased. She laughed.

"Thanks. But use your good sense."

After the girls had gone home, Susan watched her mother brush up the cookie crumbs.

"Betty, Nora, and Carol let God's love show through them today, didn't they, Mother? Do you think they knew they were doing that?"

Mrs. Grant smiled.

"They are showing you that they loved you. God has put that love in their hearts. It is part of his love and he hopes they will show it to others."

At that moment the back door banged and soon Jon rushed in, glad to see Susan at home.

"I meant to get here right after school," he told her, "but we had to practise for the musical festival. It took a long time too! Then I had to go to the store." He handed her a parcel.

"A coming-home present!" he said, grinning.

It was a book, full of riddles and puzzles, just the right kind of book to fill up some of the restless hours during the next few days to come.

"Thanks Jon!" Susan looked at her mother and smiled. Jon, too, was doing what Betty, Nora, and Carol had done.

For the next ten minutes Susan looked at the book, but her mind was not on the puzzles.

"Mother," she said at last, "know what? Marie has never had a pair of skates in her life. There's snow and ice all around her up North for months and months. She just coasts and slides."

"Well, that's fun," said Jon.

"I know, but so is skating. Mother . . ." but Susan stopped. Then she spoke up again, "Mother, you know that I want new skates for Christmas next year, but can I have some second-hand ones so that we could buy a pair for Marie too? I don't really need brand new ones."

"How nice that would be," replied Mrs. Grant. "What made you think of it?"

"Well, everybody's been so good to me. I—I want to show that I care about others too."

"I hope we can do this for you and Marie," said Mrs. Grant. "Perhaps, though, we should first discuss whether or not skates are the best gift for Marie. But no matter what we decide we will certainly help you to show your love to Marie."

chapter 23

A BUS RIDE IN THE COUNTRY

"Jon, Susan, come here!" called Mrs. Grant from the front door. "The mail-man brought us a letter from Uncle Jonathan. Come in and hear what he wants you to do!"

Jon and Susan came running. "Does he want us to visit the farm? Does he?"

"That's what he and your cousin Charles want! You both are invited for the weekend. Would you like to go?"

Jon threw his cap in the air with a shout and Susan jumped up and down. Suddenly the smile left Susan's face.

"Oh, Mother, you and Daddy are going to be at an all-day meeting on Saturday. Remember, you told us about it. How can you take us to Uncle Jonathan's?"

"Daddy and I think you and Jon can go by bus. We will put you in the bus driver's care and Uncle Jonathan can meet you at Maple Creek Crossroads. Jon, do you think you can take care of yourself and Susan?"

"Sure I can!" He looked at his sister in surprised delight. "I know the way, and what to do. We'll have fun, won't we, Sue?"

"Oh yes! I can hardly wait to see Charles' little pigs!"

Early on Saturday morning Jon and Susan found themselves on a large bus, speeding towards Uncle Jonathan's farm.

It was a lovely spring day and the countryside was fresh with green fields and roadside hedges shining in the bright sunlight.

"I hope Uncle Jonathan has a better field than that one," said Jon, pointing out of the window. "Just look at those weeds."

A white-haired lady and gentleman across the aisle smiled at him.

"You know a poor farm when you see one, don't you?" said the old gentleman. "Looks to me as if that farmer hasn't been a very good steward of his land. It's not only weedy but will likely be a patchy crop as well."

The white-haired lady peeked around her husband at them and said, "Mr. White talks of nothing else but farming, if you'll listen. We were farming folk most of our life. We love the land."

"My uncle Jonathan has a farm. We are going to visit him now," Jon told the Whites.

"My brother is named for my uncle," said Susan, "but we call him Jon."

"Uncle Jonathan loves the land too," said Jon.

"All good farmers do," said Mr. White smiling. "Now, son, the reason that field back there is so weedy and patchy is because the farmer hasn't taken care of it. Land needs good care and food just like we do. It needs rest too. You can't plant oats year after year without giving the land a rest now and then. The land is a gift from the good Lord. He expects us to care for it and use it well."

"How do you let land rest?" asked Jon. "Do you stop planting things in it?"

"That's one way. Another way is to change the kind of crop you plant. Different plants use different parts of the soil to help them grow."

"What kind of food do you feed the fields?" asked Susan. "Fields can't eat vegetables and puddings and other stuff like that, can they?"

Jon laughed. "Don't be silly, Sue."

"It's not as silly as it sounds," said Mr. White. "If vegetables were planted and not taken out of the land but cut up fine and put back in, they might be very good food, depending on what vegetable or grain it was." Mr. White smiled at Susan whose face had turned red at Jon's remark. "I suppose you could call fertilizer, which is the mixture put on the land, a form of pudding. It's sort of an extra, just like puddings are, but it helps make the land healthy."

"See!" said Susan to Jon, "I'm not silly!"

"No indeed!" said Mr. White. "The foolish one is the farmer who doesn't take proper care of his land. The Lord gives us the seed which has life already in its tiny form. We must depend on God for that. The farmer's job is to help the seed grow well so it will produce good food. Yes, the farmer must be a good steward. That means he must take care of what the Lord gives him in the best possible way."

"Does God just give the seed? Doesn't he help the farmer at all?" asked Susan. "Does the farmer have to do all the rest by himself?"

"No indeed. The Lord sends the rain and the sunshine. He has planned the seasons and the farmers must do the right things at the proper time of year. God and man work together. When you get to your uncle's farm, you'll see how it's done."

Jon looked out of the window.

We must be getting close to Maple Creek Crossing. Uncle Jonathan is meeting us there. I'll ask him, Mr. White, if he farms the way you did. I think he does, because my father told me that Uncle Jonathan is a good farmer and has a good crop nearly every year. I think he must take care of his land so the seeds will grow properly."

"Then he is a good steward of the land that the Lord gave to him," said Mr. White nodding his head.

"Maple Creek Crossing!" called out the bus driver.

Jon and Susan got ready to leave the bus. When it stopped, there were Uncle Jonathan and Charles waving to them from a station wagon. In great excitement Jon and Susan ran to meet them.

As the bus moved away, Mr. and Mrs. White who were smiling at them from the window, waved good-bye.

Jon and Susan waved back and then the station wagon sped towards the farm.

"I've got lots to show you," said Charles, "and I want you to have a ride on King, my horse. Oh, there's Karl, my friend." Charles waved at a boy who was climbing over a fence. "Karl has five little pigs and so have I. We're going to show the best pig in each litter next fall at the school fair."

"Oh!" Susan stood up to look ahead. "I can hardly wait to see your little pigs, Charles. I've seen baby pigs in pictures, but never real live ones. I can hardly wait!"

chapter 24

AS THE EARTH TURNS

"A farm is a big place!" said Susan as she looked down from a hill across the fields to the farm-house.

"You must have to work hard, Uncle Jonathan," said Jon. "What time do you get up in the morning?"

"Our rooster wakens us at sunrise," Uncle Jonathan smiled. "But I enjoy getting up early."

"How does your rooster know when to crow?" asked Susan.

Charles, who was ten years old, knew the answer to that!

"The rooster's instinct tells him," he said. "The earth turns, the sun appears and the rooster crows! Animals and people get up!"

Jon and Susan wanted to know all about farm life. Uncle Jonathan and Charles told them many things that day.

This is God's plan for an orderly world.

Day follows night.

The sun returns with its warmth and light. Sometimes we cannot see the sun because of the clouds, but it is always there giving us warmth even on winter days.

The sun awakens the plants, animals, and people to active life each day.

Animals and the farm people are at work.

Spring flowers bloom.

The sun climbs in the sky.

By the mid-day, birds and animals have had a busy time searching for food.

Farmers are enjoying dinner after a long morning's work.

The sun's rays lengthen in the afternoon and work continues in a busy world.

With sunset comes rest for most of the birds and animals and people.

Even the flowers fold their petals and appear to rest.

The cooling winds rise as darkness falls to help the world relax and sleep.

In our changing year,
spring is like the
sunrise of a day.
Spring brings new life to
the world.
Seeds are planted; the
rain falls, and the
seeds sprout.

Summer is the noon-
time of the year when the
sun warms the earth; the
rains falls, and the plants
grow and flower or bear
fruit.

123

Autumn is the afternoon of the year. Fields are ready now for the harvest.

Winter is the night-time of the year.

Days are short, brisk, and cold.

A sleeping earth rests under a warm blanket of snow, knowing that spring will not be long in coming again.

Night follows day and day follows night.

Spring, summer, autumn, and winter come as the earth moves upon its appointed way.

This is God's orderly plan for a dependable world.

chapter **25**

THE HAIL STORM

It was early evening. All Saturday afternoon, Jon and Susan had roamed about the farm with their cousin Charles. It had been a wonderful day.

"Playing with baby pigs is the most fun," said Susan to her uncle as they sat on the front porch waiting to be called to supper. "They're so cute when they wriggle and squeal."

"Riding King was more fun than that!" said Jon. "I made him gallop around the corral. It was keen."

Uncle Jonathan smiled, but his eyes were on many dark clouds that were swirling out from the western horizon.

"You're a good steward, Uncle Jonathan," Susan said suddenly.

"Why do you say that?" asked her uncle.

"Mr. White, a farmer we met on the bus, was telling us about good farming," said Jon.

"And you have such beautiful fields," went on Susan. "They're just like great wall-to-wall carpets of green. Mr. White said a farmer should be a good steward of the land."

"Oh yes! The land needs great care. So do the seeds. A farmer gets much help from nature, but he must do his part too, and often that is hard work."

"I like work—if it's outdoors," said Charles. "I'm going to be a farmer like Dad when I grow up."

"You're a farmer now," Jon told him. "You own a horse, a calf, some pigs, and some chickens."

Uncle Jonathan rubbed his hand across the short brittle ends of Charles' sunbleached hair. "And he takes care of his stock. Charles is a good steward too."

"Nature is God's working plan and a wonderful plan it is, too!" Uncle Jonathan added. Then he stood up.

"Boys, there's going to be a bad storm. Those clouds look like hail! We'd better get the stock inside. Susan, run in and tell your Aunt Ruth. She'll want to help get the chickens under cover! Follow me, boys!"

The clouds, mounting high, blotted out the sun. Wind whipped the leaves in the trees as Uncle Jonathan, Charles and Jon ran across the yard. In a matter of moments the frightened animals were inside the large barn. Aunt Ruth and Susan shut the hen-house door and then ran to bring in some blankets that were airing on the clothes-line.

Suddenly, violently, the storm broke. Rain came slashing down. Then hail fell. In the house, the hail falling on the roof beat such a fierce tattoo that no one could be heard.

Susan buried her head against Aunt Ruth's shoulder, but Jon stood at the window with Charles and Uncle Jonathan watching the ground grow white with the large hailstones, the size of small eggs.

When the storm was over a very quiet family went out into the white farmyard. Susan cried, and Charles found it hard to keep back his own tears, when they discovered that one of the tiny pigs had got away from the others and had been killed by

the hailstones. Some of Uncle Jonathan's beautiful fields of growing grain had been flattened to the ground.

Susan and Jon felt so sorry as they looked at the sad faces of their aunt and uncle and cousin.

At church the next morning they heard of other farmers who had lost cattle and all their crops.

Mr. Strong, the minister, talked about the hailstorm.

"We know why hail gathers in the clouds, and we know it must fall, but it is hard for us to understand why God allows such things to happen. Yet when everything goes well in God's world as it does most of the time, we take it all for granted, don't we? It is only when something like a bad hailstorm happens that we wonder why God lets nature destroy part of itself. These questions we cannot always answer. Some people may think that we are being punished. I do not think so. Some people may think God no longer loves them. I do not believe so. God is with us always. This is one of those times when our faith must become very strong. For faith is trust in God and in his love in spite of trouble. God is love, and now he is already at work as we plan what we can do to help one another. For we will help each other and there will also be other people outside our own neighbourhood who will come to our help."

After the sermon, the congregation stood and sang a hymn:

> O God of Bethel, by whose hand
> Thy people still are fed;
> Who through this weary pilgrimage
> Hast all our fathers led:
>
> Our vows, our prayers, we now present
> Before Thy throne of grace;
> God of our fathers, be the God
> Of their succeeding race.

When the service was over the farmers talked together, planning how they could help. Uncle Jonathan promised to give some feed to those who needed it.

The people began to smile again. They were no longer down-hearted. They had friends—good friends—who had given them courage and help in time of trouble. Jon and Susan began to feel better too.

"Yes," said Uncle Jonathan, as they drove home after church, "there are bad times in this world but sometimes the bad helps us see the good."

You might like to read from your Bible:

Galatians 6: 2 (Jesus Christ wants us to help one another)

chapter 26

LEARNING TO GROW

"Oh Mother, the hailstones were almost as big as hen's eggs," said Susan. She and Jon were home again and were telling their parents about the big storm.

"The worst thing that happened at Uncle Jonathan's farm was when Charles lost one of his baby pigs," said Jon.

"But his friend Karl lost all his little pigs because Karl and his father were not at home when the storm broke! He and Charles were going to each show a pig at the school fair next fall." Susan shook her head, remembering. "Poor Karl! We went over to see him after church and he could hardly speak to us he was so sad."

"You know what Charles did?" Jon took up the story. "He gave Karl two of his pigs. Now they each have two. I guess Charles had a hard time making up his mind to do that, but he told me that if he had lost all of his pigs, he knew Karl would share with him."

"People who live in the country often share what they have. They depend on one another to help in time of trouble. Charles learned that by watching his parents."

"I think Charles and Karl are going to be friends all their lives. Charles could do nothing but grin when he saw how happy Karl was to get the two little pigs." Jon grinned too, remembering.

Mrs. Grant smiled, as she pulled out burrs from some stockings that Susan had worn at the farm. "Sometimes it takes trouble and disaster to find out how good our friends really are."

"It doesn't sound right to me," said Jon. "Does it take trouble to find out how really good God is?"

"Yes, I think it does. If everything went well with us we might never think much of God's love. It is when we are in trouble or see someone else having a sad time that we think of God and try to do what he would want us to do in order to help make things better. It gives us a chance to show our love for others, and for others to show their love for us. Karl knows he has a real friend in Charles because he helped him in time of trouble."

"God needs people to help him," said Susan.

"God wants people to help make the world a good place in which to live," said Mr. Grant. "It is his plan that people decide what they should do to make this a better world."

"How can people know exactly what to do?" asked Jon. "Sometimes lazy people want help all the time."

"We learn about God by reading the Bible to see what Jesus believed God wanted us to do. And we pray for God's help in giving us understanding."

"And for God to give us lots of love so we can do kind things to others," added Susan. "Just like Charles did to Karl."

Jon nodded. "That was the keenest thing I ever saw. Charles giving those little pigs away. He was just crazy about those pigs."

"I remember someone who gave up a hike last week in order to stay at home because Billy, a nuisance of a boy cousin, three years younger than himself, was coming to spend the day," said Mrs. Grant.

Jon grinned, even as he turned red. "It wasn't so bad. Billy's beginning to have some sense. He would have been awful lonely with nothing to do if I hadn't stayed home."

"And I remember someone who made the last two weeks of life in the hospital exciting and fun for a little Eskimo girl, by phoning or sending a letter or a surprise in the mail every day," said Mrs. Grant.

Susan's eyes shone, as she remembered too.

"Oh, but I made such a good friend. Marie writes to me now from away in the North. We are pen pals. She is one of my very best friends."

"Love God and you love your neighbour," said Mrs. Grant. "That is the way God wants us to live in this world."

"I'm glad I live in God's world," said Jon.

"Me too!" said Susan. "And I want to know much more about it than just what's here, and on Uncle Jonathan's farm."

"You will, Sue, every day, as you grow older."

"Charles is a junior in Sunday church school," said Jon. "Next year that's what I'll be."

"Will you learn more about God's love and more stories about Jesus?" asked Susan.

"Sure. We've just begun to learn, haven't we, Mother?"

"That's right! Learning about God is something we do all our lives."

"That's good," said Jon. "I like what I've learned this year, but I've still got lots more questions to ask."

"And that's the way it should be," said Mrs. Grant, smiling, "for that's the way we learn!"

You might like to read from your Bible:

> Luke 2: 52 (Jesus grew as we must grow)
>
> 2 Timothy 3: 14-17 (The best learning is coming to know God)

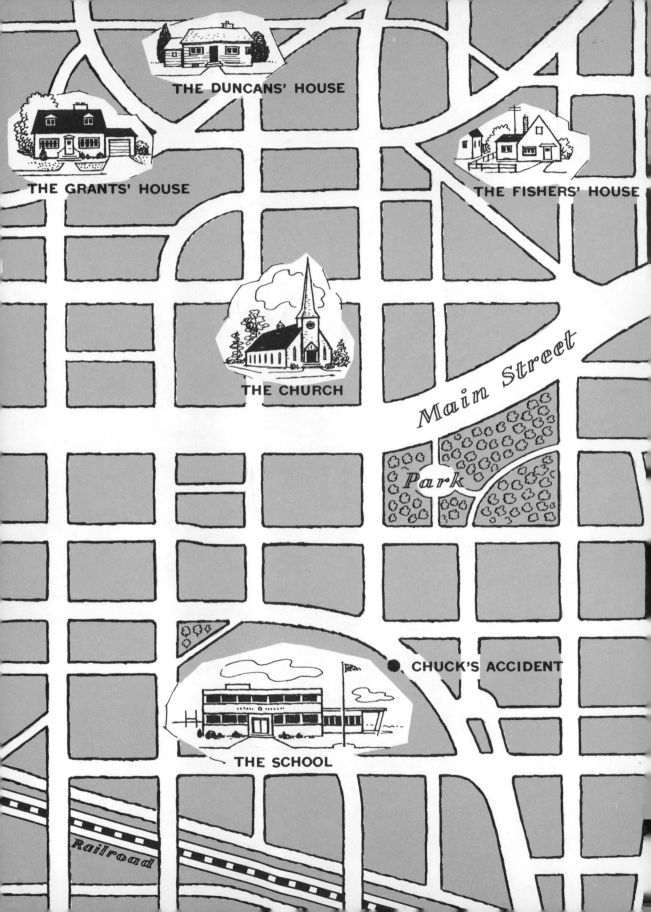

THE DUNCANS' HOUSE

THE GRANTS' HOUSE

THE FISHERS' HOUSE

THE CHURCH

Main Street

Park

CHUCK'S ACCIDENT

THE SCHOOL

Railroad